Customisable teaching resources for mathematics

USING AND APPLYING MATHEMATICS

Ages 8–9

Hilary Koll & Steve Mills

A & C Black • London

Contents

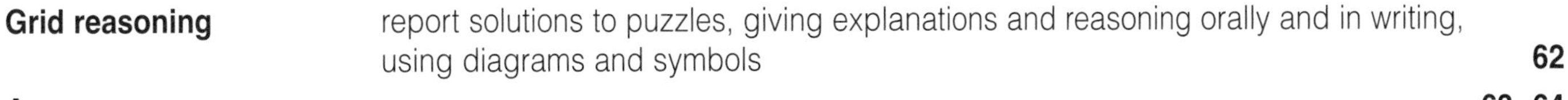

Published 2009 by A & C Black Publishers Limited
36 Soho Square, London W1D 3HB
www.acblack.com

ISBN 978-1-4081-1312-7

Editors: Lynne Williamson and Marie Lister
Designed by Billin Design Solutions Ltd

The authors and publishers would like to thank Catherine Yemm and Judith Wells for their advice in producing this series of books.

A CIP catalogue record for this book is available from the British Library.

Printed and bound in Great Britain by Halstan Printing Group.

A & C Black uses paper produced with elemental chlorine-free pulp, harvested from managed sustainable forests.

Introduction

100% New Developing Mathematics: Using and Applying Mathematics is a series of seven photocopiable activity books for children aged 4 to 11, designed to be used during the daily maths lesson. The books focus on the skills and concepts for Using and Applying Mathematics as outlined in the Primary National Strategy *Primary Framework for literacy and mathematics*. The activities are intended to be used in the time allocated to pupil activities in the daily maths lesson. They aim to reinforce the knowledge and develop the skills and understanding explored during the main part of the lesson, and to provide practice and consolidation of the learning objectives contained in the Framework document.

Using and Applying Mathematics

There are several different components which make up the **content** of maths and form the bulk of any maths curriculum:

- **mathematical facts**, for example a triangle has three sides;
- **mathematical skills**, such as counting;
- **mathematical concepts**, like place value.

For maths teaching to be successful, it is vital that children can use this mathematical content beyond their classroom, either in real-life situations or as a basis for further understanding. However, in order to do so they require extra abilities over and above the mathematical content they have learned. These extra abilities are often referred to as the **processes** of mathematical activity. It is these processes which make mathematical content usable.

As an example, consider this question:
How many triangles are there in this shape?

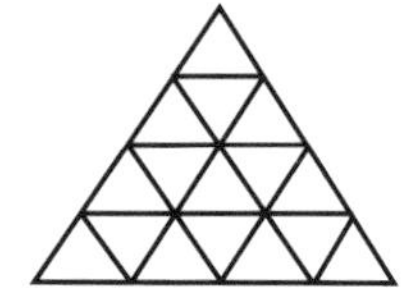

The mathematical 'content' required is only:

- the fact that a triangle has three sides.
- the **skill** of counting.

As such, it could be expected that very young children could solve this problem. The fact that they cannot suggests that other abilities are involved. These are the processes, and for this question they include:

- visualising the different-sized triangles;
- being systematic in counting all the triangles of different sizes;
- looking for patterns in the numbers of triangles;
- trial and error;
- recording.

Unless children can apply these processes in this situation, then however good their counting skills and knowledge of triangles may be, they will fail.

The strand 'Using and applying mathematics' of the *Primary Framework for mathematics* emphasises the importance of using and talking about mathematics in real situations. This series of books is intended to make more explicit the processes involved in learning how to put one's maths to use.

Using and Applying Mathematics Ages 8–9 supports the development of the using and applying processes by providing a series of activities that create opportunities to introduce and practise them through a series of activities. On the whole the activities are designed for children to work on independently, either individually, in pairs or in groups.

Pre-school children are naturally inquisitive about the world around them. They like to explore and experiment, and to make marks and record things on paper in their own idiosyncratic ways. Unfortunately, once at school, the focus is often placed firmly on the maths 'content' alone and children can be led to believe that maths is not a subject of exploration, but rather one of simply learning the 'right way to do things'. As a result, when older children are asked to explore and investigate maths they are often at a loss if their maths teaching to date has not encouraged and built upon their natural instincts.

Ages 8–9 helps children to develop the following processes:

- predicting
- visualising
- looking for pattern
- recording
- reasoning
- making decisions
- estimating
- explaining
- being systematic
- co-operating
- comparing
- testing ideas
- trial and improvement
- asking own questions

When using these activities, the focus need not be on the actual mathematical 'content'. Instead, the teacher's demonstrations, discussions and questioning should emphasise the processes the children are using. When appropriate, invite the children to explain their thinking to others. Research has shown that children develop processes most successfully when the teacher encourages pupils to act as experts rather than novices, granting them more autonomy, and encouraging a range of approaches to any problem rather than constraining discussion to produce an overall class plan. The children should evaluate their own plans against other plans in the posing, planning and monitoring phases of the lessons.

Ages 8–9 helps children with Solving Problems, Representing, Enquiring, Reasoning and Communicating, as recommended in the revised Primary Framework. These five themes, although identified separately in the table which follows, are interlinked.

Using and applying mathematics	*Solving problems*	*Representing*	*Enquiring*	*Reasoning*	*Communicating*
Year 4	Solve one-step and two-step problems involving numbers, money or measures, including time; choose and carry out appropriate calculations, using calculator methods where appropriate	Represent a puzzle or problem using number sentences, statements or diagrams; use these to solve the problem; present and interpret the solution in the context of the problem	Suggest a line of enquiry and the strategy needed to follow it; collect, organise and interpret selected information to find answers	Identify and use patterns, relationships and properties of numbers or shapes; investigate a statement involving numbers and test it with examples	Report solutions to puzzles and problems, giving explanations and reasoning orally and in writing, using diagrams and symbols

Extension

Many of the activity sheets end with a challenge (**Now try this!**), which reinforces and extends children's learning, and provides the teacher with an opportunity for assessment. These might include harder questions, with numbers from a higher range, than those in the main part of the activity sheet. Some challenges are open-ended questions and provide opportunity for children to think mathematically for themselves. Occasionally the challenge will require additional paper or that the children write on the reverse of the sheet itself. Many of the activities encourage children to generate their own questions or puzzles for a partner to solve.

Organisation

Very little equipment is needed, but it will be useful to have available: coloured pencils, counters, cubes, scissors, glue, coins, squared paper, number lines, grids and tracks.

Where possible, the children's work should be supported by ICT equipment, such as number lines and tracks on interactive whiteboards, or computer software for comparing and ordering numbers. It is also vital that children's experiences are introduced in real-life contexts and through practical activities. The teachers' notes at the foot of each page and the more detailed notes on pages 6 to 11 suggest ways in which this can be done effectively.

To help teachers select appropriate learning experiences for the children, the activities are grouped into sections within the book. However, the activities are not expected to be used in this order unless stated otherwise. The sheets are intended to support, rather than direct, the teacher's planning.

Some activities can be made easier or more challenging by masking or substituting numbers. You may wish to re-use pages by copying them onto card and laminating them.

Accompanying CD

The enclosed CD-ROM contains all of the activity sheets from the book and a program that allows you to edit them for printing or saving. This means that modifications can be made to further differentiate the activities to suit individual pupils' needs. See page 12 for further details.

Teachers' notes

Brief notes are provided at the foot of each page, giving ideas and suggestions for maximising the effectiveness of the activity sheets. These can be masked before copying.

Further explanations of the activities can be found on pages 6 to 11, together with examples of questions that you can ask.

Whole-class warm-up activities

The following activities provide some practical ideas that can be used to introduce or reinforce the main teaching part of the lesson, or provide an interesting basis for discussion.

Make up a story

Write a number statement on the board, such as $30 \div 5 = 6$, and ask the children, in pairs, to devise a story to match the statement, for example: *Thirty children played football in the Games lesson. Each team had five players and there were six teams.* Ask the class to decide which was the most interesting story. Include questions that contain a missing number other than the answer, for example: $28 - \square = 19$, $\square + 29 = 58$.

Targets

Write several numbers on the board (such as 80, 50, 9, 6, 4), and a target number (for example 244). Set the children the challenge of hitting or getting as close as possible to the target number, using some or all of the numbers and operations of their choice (example: $9 - 6 = 3$, $3 \times 80 = 240$, and $240 + 4 = 244$).

Hit or miss?

The constant function facility on a calculator is a useful way to explore decimals. Write a sequence rule, for example: 'Start at 1 and count on in jumps of 0·2'. Ask the children to predict whether the sequence will 'hit' or 'miss' other numbers, for example: *Will it hit 3 or 4·5 or 11?* Provide the children with calculators and ask them to check their predictions by continuing the patterns using the constant function facility, for example pressing these keys (check with the calculator manual if necessary).
1 + + 0·2 = = = = = = etc.

Twenty questions

Hide a 3-D shape in a bag and ask the children to find out which shape it is by asking questions. You can only answer *yes* or *no* to their questions. Challenge the children to guess the shape in twenty questions.

Notes on the activities

Solve one-step and two-step problems involving numbers, money or measures, including time; choose and carry out appropriate calculations, using calculator methods where appropriate

This aspect of Using and Applying Mathematics deals with Solving Problems. It is central to all mathematics and if children are unable to solve problems, then the mathematics that they know is wasted. Children need to develop confidence in tackling problems without looking to teachers or other children for help. They should learn to decide which facts are key to the problem, make decisions about what operations to use and then follow them through, checking to see whether their answer is a sensible one.

Codebreaker (page 13)

Processes: make decisions, record, reason, explain

These problems require the children to make their own decisions as to how to answer the questions. The children should be encouraged to describe these methods and strategies and demonstrate how different equipment, such as 100-squares and number lines, could be used to help them reach answers.

SUGGESTED QUESTIONS:

- How did you work out the answer to this question?
- How did you know what to do?
- Can you show me what method you used for this question?
- How did you know to multiply?

Be a detective (page 14)

Processes: reason, record, make decisions

Allow the children to make their own decisions about what the number must be, based on the clues. Encourage them to write all the possible numbers for each clue and then to find which number appears in both lists. Revise the meaning of the word 'product' before beginning.

SUGGESTED QUESTIONS:

- How did you find this solution?
- What does the word 'product' mean?
- How could you write this as a number sentence?

Market stall (page 15)

Processes: reason, record, explain

Allow the children to make their own decisions about what to do and encourage them to use number sentences or pictorial methods on the back of the worksheet to record their working. As a further extension, the children could be asked to find out how much change each person would get from a £10 or a £20 note.

SUGGESTED QUESTION:

- How did you find this solution?

Sheila's shopping basket (page 16)

Processes: explain, reason, record

At the start of the lesson, ask the children to tell a partner all the units of measure that they know and the relationships between them. Check that they know that 1000 g = 1 kg, and 1000 ml = 1 l.

SUGGESTED QUESTIONS:

- How did you work out this answer?
- Did you have to find the exact amount?
- Was it always necessary to work out the exact answer to the multiplication?

Badge sale (page 17)

Processes: reason, make decisions, explain

Discuss strategies that the children chose to work out the answers, drawing attention to the use of equipment such as number lines, 100-squares, coins, counting materials, or other written or mental methods.

SUGGESTED QUESTIONS:

- How did you find the answer?
- What method did you use to find the answer?
- Did you use the same method for each question or did you do anything different on this question? Why was that?

Fair share: 1 and 2 (pages 18 and 19)

Processes: reason, make decisions, explain, be systematic

Observe the methods that the children use to find the answers, for example noting which children use the picture, their fingers, equipment, or a mental method.

SUGGESTED QUESTIONS/PROMPT:

- How easy did you find this?
- Did you find the answer straight away?
- Can you find other answers? How do you know that you have found them all?
- Let's write a class list of all the possible answers we can find.

Reading the signs (page 20)

Processes: reason, make decisions, record

The children should work in pairs and decide upon the appropriate calculations for each problem to show what they think should be done. Encourage the children to draw diagrams to help them to visualise the problems.

SUGGESTED QUESTIONS:

- How did you find this solution?
- Can you explain why these two road sign questions require a different calculation?

Post office problems (page 21)

Processes: reason, explain, record

The children could work together in pairs on this activity to promote discussion. Revise equivalent units of mass and decimals to one decimal place. Talk about strategies for answering each question and encourage the children to describe the methods they used.

SUGGESTED QUESTIONS:

- How did you find this solution?
- What strategies did you use?

Container problems: 1 and 2 (pages 22 and 23)

Processes: reason, make decisions

At the start of the lesson, remind the children about the notation 'ml' and 'l', and that 1000 ml is the same as 1 l.

These worksheets provide opportunity for the children to determine which calculation is necessary to solve problems involving capacity. The problems are varied and require considerable thought and the children should discuss in pairs their thoughts and reasoning. When the children are recording number sentences, they could be shown how to write each situation using a missing number, rather than the last number always being the answer. Some situations may require more than one calculation.

SUGGESTED QUESTIONS:

- How did you find this solution?
- If you can't find the answer, is it because the answer is in millilitres rather than litres?

Loopy witches (page 24)

Processes: reason, make decisions

At the start of the lesson, remind the children about the notation 'ml' and 'l', and that 1000 ml is the same as 1 l. As a quick way of checking the answers to this worksheet, the letters at the bottom right of each card will spell 'BROOMSTICK'. This activity could also be used as an oral and mental starter.

SUGGESTED QUESTIONS:

- How did you find this solution?
- If you can't find the answer, is it because the answer is in millilitres rather than litres?

Time teaser (page 25)

Processes: reason, make decisions, explain

As a quick way of checking the answers to this worksheet, the only clock left unmatched shows the time 9:18 pm.

SUGGESTED QUESTIONS:

- How would you say this time in words?
- Can you show me this time on a clock face?
- Is this in the morning, the afternoon, or the evening?

Taxi! (page 26)

Processes: reason, make own decisions

For this activity, the children should be familiar with 'am' and 'pm' notation, and with times written in digital form. The times in the questions and answers could be altered to provide further practice of this type of problem solving.

SUGGESTED QUESTIONS:

- How did you find the answer?
- Did you look at a clock face?
- Did you add or subtract the minutes or hours first?

Story-telling (page 27)

Processes: ask own questions, make decisions, explain, record

This activity encourages children to think of their own stories to match given calculations. Provide a range of examples and contexts for the children to think about before beginning this worksheet, for example shopping with money, numbers of sweets/vegetables/pieces of fruit, measurement contexts.

SUGGESTED QUESTIONS:

- What could your story be about?
- What has to happen?

Calculator calamities: 1 and 2 (pages 28 and 29)

Processes: reason, explain, record

These problems involve understanding how mistakes can be corrected using inverses, or by adjusting calculations.

SUGGESTED PROMPT/QUESTION:

- Describe in words what Meena's mistake is.
- How could she correct it?

Represent a puzzle or problem using number sentences, statements or diagrams; use these to solve the problem; present and interpret the solution in the context of the problem

The next theme of the Framework's Using and Applying strand deals with Representing. It focuses on children making sense of a problem or puzzle and organising the information in a way that enables them to solve it. In the early years, children may rely on practical materials and diagrams, but as they develop confidence in this area they may move on to using numbers, calculations and other modelling, including tables, lists or even the use of algebra.

Quiz show (page 30)

Processes: explain, reason, make decisions

This worksheet provides the children with the opportunity to consider and identify which operations are necessary in solving each question.

SUGGESTED QUESTIONS:

- Why do you think you should use that calculation?
- What words in the question show that it should be that operation?

Number sentences (page 31)

Processes: reason, make decisions, compare, explain

It is important that the children understand that more than one number sentence can represent each situation. Encourage discussion of each number sentence and ask the children whether they can think of further ways that the situation could be represented.

SUGGESTED QUESTIONS:

- Which of these are possible ways of showing the situation?

- Can you think of any other ways?
- Which way would you have shown it?

Café life (page 32)

Processes: reason, explain, record

This worksheet provides the children with the opportunity to consider and identify which operations are necessary in solving each question. It may be necessary for more than one number sentence to be used. Watch out for incorrect number sentences that merge two together, for example where a child incorrectly writes $32 \div 4 = 8 \times 3 = 24$, rather than $32 \div 4 = 8$, $8 \times 3 = 24$. Draw attention to the need to be careful when dealing with pounds and pence.

SUGGESTED QUESTIONS:

- How did you find the answer?
- Which questions did you find the hardest? Why?
- How did you write this as a number sentence or number sentences?

Billy the Baker's cakes (page 33)

Processes: trial and improvement, test ideas, record, explain, reason

Encourage the children to notice patterns in the numbers, for example to realise that three rows of five will have the same number of buns as five rows of three.

SUGGESTED QUESTIONS:

- What patterns did you use to help you?
- What patterns did you notice?
- How do you know you have found all the solutions?

How? (page 34)

Processes: explain, reason, ask own questions, record

This activity encourages the children to describe the strategies they would use to answer a calculation and to consider the different ways that this could be done. Calculations can be altered to provide differentiation.

SUGGESTED QUESTIONS:

- What would you do?
- Would you use any equipment?
- Could you show me this on a number line/ 100-square?
- What other ways could it be done?

Measuring methods (page 35)

Processes: visualise, make decisions, reason

During the plenary, ask the children to demonstrate the methods that they used. In particular, ask the children to explain any

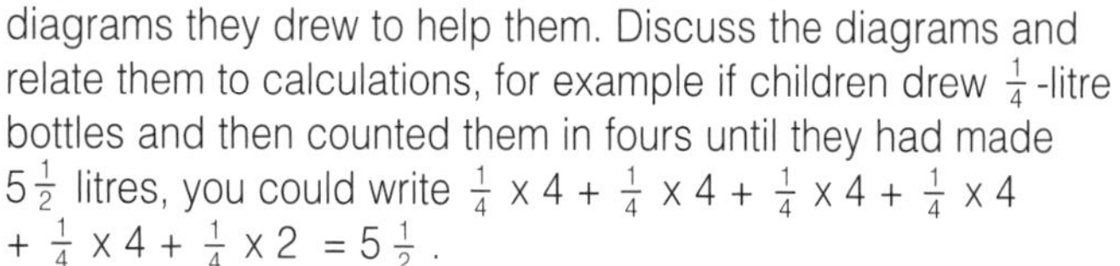

diagrams they drew to help them. Discuss the diagrams and relate them to calculations, for example if children drew $\frac{1}{4}$-litre bottles and then counted them in fours until they had made $5\frac{1}{2}$ litres, you could write $\frac{1}{4} \times 4 + \frac{1}{4} \times 4 + \frac{1}{4} \times 4 + \frac{1}{4} \times 4 + \frac{1}{4} \times 4 + \frac{1}{4} \times 2 = 5\frac{1}{2}$.

SUGGESTED QUESTION:

- How did you find this solution?

Coin contest (page 36)

Processes: make decisions, predict, test ideas, be systematic, reason, look for pattern

All numbers from 6p to 60p can be made with six coins, and all but 38p, 39p, 48p and 49p can be made with only four coins. Encourage the children to work systematically, for example by swapping a 1p for a 2p in each of these solutions, and to look for patterns in the coins used.

SUGGESTED QUESTIONS:

- How could you present or report your findings to others?
- What is the clearest way of showing the results to others?

Sour grapes (page 37)

Processes: be systematic, generalise, compare, record, look for pattern, reason, predict, test ideas

Remind the children that they can check their solutions by ensuring the totals of each addition add to make the number of grapes. The children could compare solutions and collectively write a class list. Discuss strategies that the children used to help them find the solutions, for example: 'For six grapes I used the answers to five grapes and wrote out the 15 five-grape solutions with '1 +' in front of them.

SUGGESTED QUESTIONS/PROMPT:

- Could you do the same grapes but in a different order?
- Do you notice any patterns? Explain them to us.
- What strategies did you use?
- What if there were seven or eight grapes?

Field event (page 38)

Processes: visualise, make decisions, reason, test ideas, look for pattern

In the extension activity, encourage the children to try different multiples of 5 and to look for patterns in the solutions. More confident children may be able to begin to generalise and predict other solutions.

SUGGESTED QUESTIONS:

- How did you find this solution?
- Have you checked each rule against your answers?
- If you were to do this again, would you try a different way?

Tent teaser (page 39)

Processes: visualise, make decisions, reason, be systematic, test ideas

Remind the children that they do not necessarily need to work through the clues in order.

SUGGESTED QUESTIONS:

- How did you find this solution?
- Have you checked each rule against your answers?
- If you were to do this again, would you try a different way?

Sheep and goats (page 40)

Processes: visualise, make decisions, reason, be systematic, test ideas

Encourage the children to use words or pictures to explain why each statement is true or false.

SUGGESTED QUESTIONS/PROMPT:

- Can you show me how you know whether this statement is true or false?
- Look at Sam's explanation. Can you see how he worked this one out?

Suggest a line of enquiry and the strategy needed to follow it; collect, organise and interpret selected information to find answers

This theme encourages children to pursue lines of enquiry. Initially, children learn to ask questions and go on to develop skills of planning, organisation and decision-making. Children need to be taught how to use pictures, lists and diagrams when organising information and supporting their line of enquiry.

Fruit segments (page 41)

Processes: explain, ask own questions, reason

This activity can help the children to see how many different questions can be asked about a context, and encourages them to make up their own questions.

SUGGESTED QUESTIONS:

- How many different questions have we asked in our class?
- How would you answer Jo's question?
- How many different ways did you find?

Thinking thimbles (page 42)

Processes: be systematic, check, compare, visualise, look for pattern, record

Ensure the children realise that in this activity, there does not have to be a different number of thimbles on each shelf: it is possible to have the same number on each shelf. Discuss whether this means that there will be more or fewer answers than if there has to be a different number of thimbles on each shelf. (There are more possible answers.)

SUGGESTED QUESTIONS:

- What have you discovered?
- How can you be sure that you have found all the ways?
- Did you sort them in a particular way?
- How could you check?
- Were you systematic?

Book counting (page 43)

Processes: make decisions, record, co-operate, predict, be systematic

This worksheet encourages the children to work together to make decisions and to plan how to go about collecting information about the number of books in a library area.

SUGGESTED QUESTIONS:

- How did you decide what to do?
- How well did you work together as a group?
- What do you think the outcome might be?
- Were you systematic?

Planning enquiries: 1 and 2 (pages 44 and 45)

Processes: make decisions, record, co-operate, predict

These worksheets encourage the children to make decisions and to plan how to follow lines of enquiry by collecting data.

SUGGESTED QUESTIONS:

- How did you decide what to do?
- What do you think the outcome might be?

Identify and use patterns, relationships and properties of numbers or shapes; investigate a statement involving numbers and test it with examples

Reasoning should go on in all areas of Using and Applying Mathematics. This theme focuses on making deductions based on patterns, properties and relationships. The children should be encouraged to hear and develop the language and vocabulary of reasoning, and to use logical steps when reasoning.

Confetti colours (page 46)

Processes: visualise, compare, reason

Explain to the children that when something is 'next to' another it can be horizontally or vertically next to it, but not diagonally. For example in question 3, the horseshoe shape is next to the two stars; it is not classed as being next to any of the other three shapes.

SUGGESTED QUESTIONS:

- How easy did you find this?
- Did you work through the clues in order?
- Would it have helped if you had worked through in a different order?

Shelf stacking and shelf stacking clues (pages 47 and 48)

Processes: trial and improvement, test ideas, record, explain, reason

Note that the order of the clues does not always mean that information can be used when first read. The children should continue reading the clues and then go back and determine which information can now be found out.

SUGGESTED QUESTION/ PROMPT:

- Why was this set of clues more difficult?
- Tell me where the tripod is in your answer.

The rules of the rows (page 49)

Processes: trial and improvement, test ideas, record, explain, reason, be systematic, look for pattern

Encourage the children to work systematically. Some children will begin to notice that, to an extent, they can use one set of answers to help them find the next, for example by doubling the numbers.

For the extension activity, compile a class list of the different possible rules for the hexagons.

SUGGESTED QUESTIONS:

- What patterns did you use to help you?
- What patterns did you notice?

Necklace numbers (page 50)

Processes: visualise, compare, look for pattern, test ideas, trial and improvement

Encourage the children to look for patterns and to describe them to others.

SUGGESTED QUESTION:

- What is the rule for this sequence?

Sticks (page 51)

Processes: reason, visualise, explain

Encourage the children to describe their reasoning and invite them to explain their thinking to others.

SUGGESTED QUESTIONS:

- How did you work out the solutions?
- What did this clue tell you?
- Which was the most helpful clue?

Tell me (page 52)

Processes: explain, co-operate, compare, record

Since each card shows a triangle and a rectangle, this activity focuses attention on describing accurately what each looks like and where they lie in relation to each other. Encourage the children to use specific language, such as those words in the box on the worksheet, making sure that their descriptions cannot also apply to other cards. For example, 'There is an equilateral triangle and a rectangle' applies to more than one card.

Shapes and descriptions can be mounted on a wall as puzzles for the children to solve, and as a lively and stimulating display.

SUGGESTED QUESTIONS:

- In what way is this card different from this one?
- How could you describe this card?
- Which word could you use to describe where the triangle is?
- What about the rectangle?
- Does your description only fit that card, or could it describe one of the others ones too?

True statements (page 53)

Processes: look for pattern, compare, be systematic

At the start of the lesson, revise all the terms used on the worksheet.

SUGGESTED QUESTIONS:

- Have you found all the possible true statements?
- How can you be sure?

Dividing exactly (page 54)

Processes: look for pattern, test ideas, predict, reason

At the start of the lesson, practise different times-tables and write these on the board. Ask the children to pick out numbers that appear as answers in different tables, and to explain what that means, for example 30 is in the 2 times-table, the 3 times-table, the 5 times-table and the 10 times-table. That means that it divides exactly by 2, 3, 5 and 10.

SUGGESTED QUESTION:

- What is special about multiples of 3/4/5/6/7/8/9/10?

Halfway house (page 55)

Processes: look for pattern, explain, reason, compare, record, justify, test ideas

Encourage the children to give different examples that show when a statement is true or false.

SUGGESTED QUESTIONS:

- How do you know that that statement is true?
- Why isn't one example enough to show that that statement is true?

Hard cards (page 56)

Processes: reason, test ideas, explain

Encourage the children to try examples to help them to decide whether an answer will be odd or even, for example the answer to 3 add 4 is odd. As a further extension, the children could draw diagrams, for example of sets of counters in pairs and 'odd ones', to accompany each card to show why the answers are as given.

SUGGESTED QUESTIONS:

- What does the term 'product' mean?
- How do you know it will always be even/odd?

Report solutions to puzzles and problems, giving explanations and reasoning orally and in writing, using diagrams and symbols

The final theme is Communicating, including both oral and recorded communications. Children should be given opportunities to express their thinking, their reasoning and to communicate their findings to others, and also to make personal records of their own. In lessons, children should be encouraged to work with others, discussing decisions to be made, describing actions taken and conclusions made.

Number puzzles (page 57)

Processes: look for pattern, reason, explain

Provide the children with number squares to help them with this activity if necessary.

SUGGESTED QUESTION:

- Can you explain how you worked this out?

3 for 2! (page 58)

Processes: reason, explain

The children could make up their own offers for others to investigate. They should be encouraged to report their findings to the class.

SUGGESTED QUESTION:

- Can you explain how you worked this out?

Marble run (page 59)

Processes: visualise, trial and improvement, test ideas, explain

Encourage the children to focus on describing strategies they developed when looking for solutions.

SUGGESTED QUESTION:

- Can you explain how you worked this out?

In a flap (page 60)

Processes: explain, reason, ask own questions

At the start of the lesson, ask the children to give the inverse operations for addition, subtraction, multiplication and division. Write a missing number problem on the board, for example 53 – □ = 78, and ask the children how they would solve it.

SUGGESTED QUESTIONS:

- What would you do?
- Which calculation did you do to help you find the missing number?
- What other ways could it be done?

What a puzzle! (page 61)

Processes: explain, compare, reason

At the start of the lesson, write a vertical addition on the board (for example for 286 + 347 =), and ask the children to describe the steps they take to work out the answer (633). Erase some of the digits, and ask the children how they could use the digits that are left to work out the missing digits. What calculations would they use? Would they use an inverse operation?

SUGGESTED QUESTIONS:

- How did you work this out?
- What was your thinking?
- How could you explain this on paper/in words?

Grid reasoning (page 62)

Processes: explain, reason, test ideas, trial and improvement, visualise

This challenging activity encourages the children to persevere in a problem-solving activity, and to describe the strategies they used.

SUGGESTED QUESTIONS:

- Did you manage to solve the problem?
- What was your thinking?
- What did you learn?
- If you were going to do it again, what would you do differently?

Using the CD-ROM

The CD-ROM included with this book contains an easy-to-use software program that allows you to print out pages from the book, to view them (e.g. on an interactive whiteboard) or to customise the activities to suit the needs of your pupils.

Getting started

It's easy to run the software. Simply insert the CD-ROM into your CD drive and the disk should autorun and launch the interface in your web browser.

If the disk does not autorun, open 'My Computer' and select the CD drive, then open the file 'start.html'.

Please note: this CD-ROM is designed for use on a PC. It will also run on most Apple Macintosh computers in Safari however, due to the differences between Mac and PC fonts, you may experience some unavoidable variations in the typography and page layouts of the activity sheets.

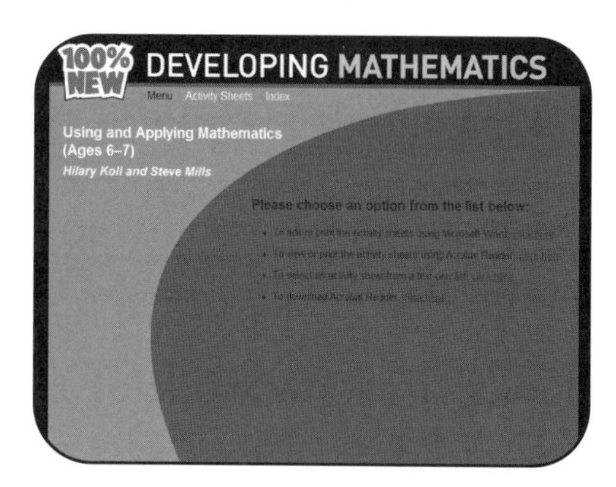

The Menu screen

Four options are available to you from the main menu screen.

The first option takes you to the Activity Sheets screen, where you can choose an activity sheet to edit or print out using Microsoft Word.

(If you do not have the Microsoft Office suite, you might like to consider using OpenOffice instead. This is a multi-platform and multi-lingual office suite, and an 'open-source' project. It is compatible with all other major office suites, and the product is free to download, use and distribute. The homepage for OpenOffice on the Internet is: www.openoffice.org.)

The second option on the main menu screen opens a PDF file of the entire book using Adobe Reader (see below). This format is ideal for printing out copies of the activity sheets or for displaying them, for example on an interactive whiteboard.

The third option allows you to choose a page to edit from a text-only list of the activity sheets, as an alternative to the graphical interface on the Activity Sheets screen.

Adobe Reader is free to download and to use. If it is not already installed on your computer, the fourth link takes you to the download page on the Adobe website.

You can also navigate directly to any of the three screens at any time by using the tabs at the top.

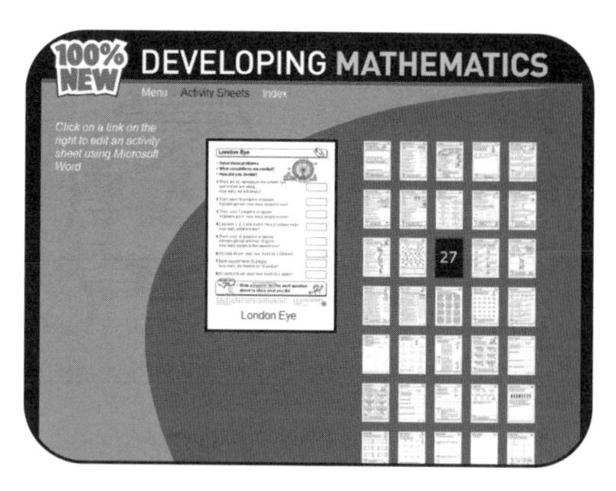

The Activity Sheets screen

This screen shows thumbnails of all the activity sheets in the book. Rolling the mouse over a thumbnail highlights the page number and also brings up a preview image of the page.

Click on the thumbnail to open a version of the page in Microsoft Word (or an equivalent software program, see above.) The full range of editing tools are available to you here to customise the page to suit the needs of your particular pupils. You can print out copies of the page or save a copy of your edited version onto your computer.

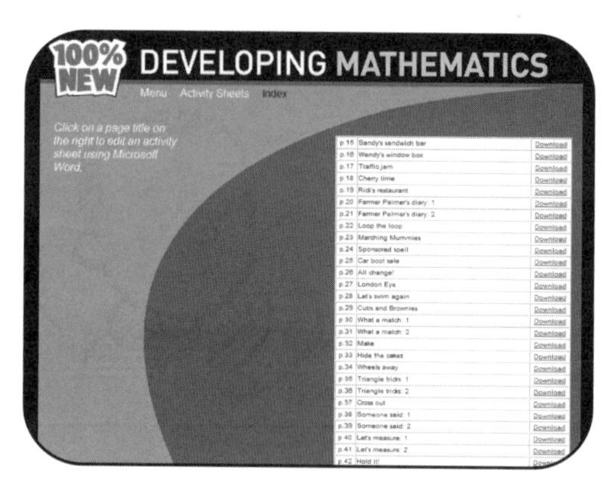

The Index screen

This is a text-only version of the Activity Sheets screen described above. Choose an activity sheet and click on the 'download' link to open a version of the page in Microsoft Word to edit or print out.

Technical support

If you have any questions regarding the *100% New Developing Literacy* or *Developing Mathematics* software, please email us at the address below. We will get back to you as quickly as possible.

educationalsales@acblack.com

Codebreaker

- **Find each answer in the grid and write the number and letter.**

The letters spell out a code word.

10 E	148 D	324 U	9 O
19 N	100 R	55 V	45 I
46 C	102 E	8 A	60 R

1 A coach holds 54 people. If six full coaches go to a football match, how many people go by coach?

324
U

2 Ali swims 32 lengths and Jo swims 51 lengths. What is the difference?

3 Sam has 37 stickers and Kai has three times as many. How many stickers do they have altogether?

4 One-quarter of 136 children eat school meals. How many children do **not** eat school meals?

5 There are 150 children in a school. If two-thirds of the children are girls, how many girls are there?

6 How many apples are needed so that 91 children can each have half an apple?

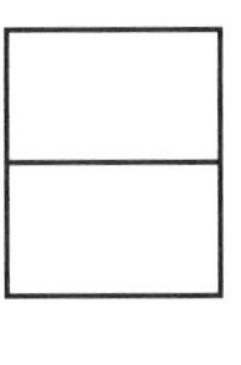

7 In a class of 32, five children are away. If the others are put into three equal groups, how many children are in each group?

8 A book has 96 pages. If Kim reads 12 pages on day 1 and 29 on day 2, how many pages has she left to read?

9 A factory makes 99 bottles every day. How many days will it take the factory to make over 900 bottles?

10 If there are 15 sheep in a field, how many legs are there altogether?

Code word: U __ __ __ __ __ __ __ __ __

Teachers' note Encourage the children to show their working out on a separate piece of paper. As an extension, ask the children to say which of the following questions will give the largest answer: 26 × 5, 600 ÷ 4, 42 + 79, 200 − 57.

Be a detective

• **With a partner, find the number that matches the clues.**

1 **Clues**

The number is between 40 and 50.
When it is divided by 5 there is a remainder of 2.
When it is multiplied by 2 the answer is more than 90.

The number is

2 **Clues**

The number is between 50 and 70.
When it is divided by 4 there is no remainder.
The sum of its digits is 6.

The number is 

3 **Clues**

The number is between 61 and 79.
It is a multiple of 5.
The product of its digits is 0.

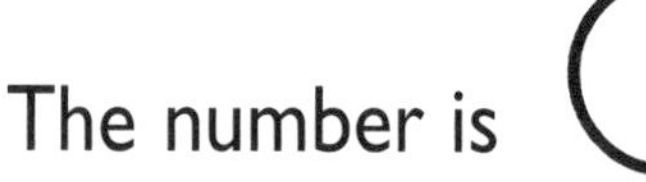

The number is

4 **Clues**

The number is between 40 and 60.
When it is doubled the answer is a multiple of 10.
When it is divided by 6 there is a remainder of 3.

The number is

5 **Clues**

The number is between 40 and 90.
When it is divided by 7 there is a remainder of 4.
It is a square number.

The number is

6 **Clues**

The number is between 20 and 99.
The number is a square number.
The product of its two digits is a square number.

The number is 

7 **Clues**

The number is between 76 and 86.
The sum of the digits is odd.
The product of the digits is a multiple of 10.

The number is 

8 **Clues**

The number is between 40 and 60.
When it is divided by 5 there is no remainder.
When it is divided by 7 there is a remainder of 3.

The number is 

Teachers' note Some children will benefit from having a number line and multiplication tables displayed, to which they can refer. If preferred, the worksheet can be cut into cards so that the children can concentrate on one set of clues at a time.

Market stall

• **Work out how much each person spent.**

Teachers' note As an extension, the children can make up their own questions for a partner to solve. Remind them to think carefully about whether the amounts are given in pence or pounds. The prices can be altered to more difficult numbers, for example £1.37 for a pineapple and 79p per kilogram for tomatoes, to provide more challenging calculations.

Sheila's shopping basket

- **How many of each item must Sheila buy?**

1 Sheila needs
1 kg of flour.

She needs ___ bags.

2 Sheila needs
500 g of chocolate.

She needs ___ bars.

3 Sheila needs
775 g of butter.

She needs ___ packs.

4 Sheila needs
800 g of sugar.

She needs ___ bags.

5 Sheila needs
1 kg of raisins.

She needs ___ bags.

6 Sheila needs
650 g of cocoa.

She needs ___ tins.

7 Sheila needs
575 ml of cream.

She needs ___ pots.

8 Sheila needs
1 litre of custard.

She needs ___ cartons.

NOW TRY THIS!

- **On the back of this sheet, work out how much of each ingredient Sheila will have left over.**

Teachers' note Ensure the children understand that, most of the time, Sheila must buy more than the amount she actually needs so that she has sufficient for the recipes she is following. Encourage the children to explain their methods and to describe the strategies that they used for finding the answers.

Badge sale

The children of Hawsker school have made badges to sell at the school fête.

	Shields	Stars	Flowers	Circles
large				
small				

1 Three small shields cost 60p. How much do five small shields cost?

2 Two large circles cost £1.60. How much do three large circles cost?

3 Three large stars cost £4.50. How much do two large stars cost?

4 Four small flowers cost 48p. How much do five small flowers cost?

5 Five small circles cost £1. How much do three small circles cost?

6 Four large shields cost £5.20. How much do three large shields cost?

7 Three small stars cost 75p. How much do seven small stars cost?

8 Five large flowers cost £5.50. How much do three large flowers cost?

NOW TRY THIS!

James buys one of each badge.

- **How much does it cost?**

Teachers' note Ensure that the children understand that the price given for several items is the total price for that number, and not the price for one of the items. Encourage the children to describe the strategies that they used for solving the problems, using words, diagrams or calculations.

Fair share: 1

Mrs Joseph puts £10 notes into six envelopes. She puts £10 in the first envelope, £20 in the second envelope, and so on.

£10 £20 £30 £40 £50 £60

1 How much money is there in total? ________

2 Mrs Joseph gives two envelopes to each of her three nieces. Which envelopes does she give each child so that they each have the same amount?

________________ ________________ ________________

3 If Mrs Joseph had eight envelopes, how much money would there be in total? ________

£10 £20 £30 £40 £50 £60 £70 £80

4 How could she give each child the same amount this time?

________________ ________________ ________________

NOW TRY THIS!

- **Find other ways of sharing out the eight envelopes to give each child the same amount of money.**

Teachers' note Use in conjunction with page 19, Fair share: 2. Encourage the children to decide for themselves how to work out the solutions, for example using a cube to represent each £10 note or writing the amounts on slips of paper. Compile a class list of all the possible solutions to the eight envelopes problem.

Fair share: 2

Mr Barber puts £10 notes into envelopes. He puts £10 in the first envelope, £20 in the second envelope, and so on.

£10 £20 £30 £40 £50 £60 £70 £80

1 How much money is there in total? ______

2 Mr Barber gives two envelopes to each of his four children. Which envelopes does he give each child so that they each have the same amount?

__________ __________ __________ __________

3 If Mr Barber had nine envelopes, how much money would there be in total? ______

£10 £20 £30 £40 £50 £60 £70 £80 £90

4 How could he give **three** of his children the same amount?

______________ ______________ ______________

NOW TRY THIS!

- **Find other ways of sharing out the nine envelopes to give three of his children the same amount of money.**

Teachers' note Use in conjunction with page 18, Fair share: 1. Encourage the children to decide for themselves how to work out the solutions, for example using a cube to represent each £10 note or writing the amounts on slips of paper. Compile a class list of all the possible solutions to the nine envelopes problem.

Reading the signs

Jack likes to drive his car.
He sees lots of road signs on his trips.

- **Work with a partner to answer the questions.**

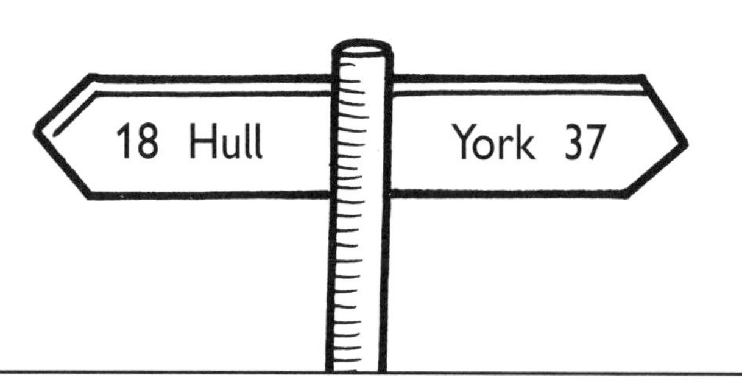

1 How many miles is it from Hull to York along this road?

_____ miles

2 How many miles is it from Cambridge to London along this road?

_____ miles

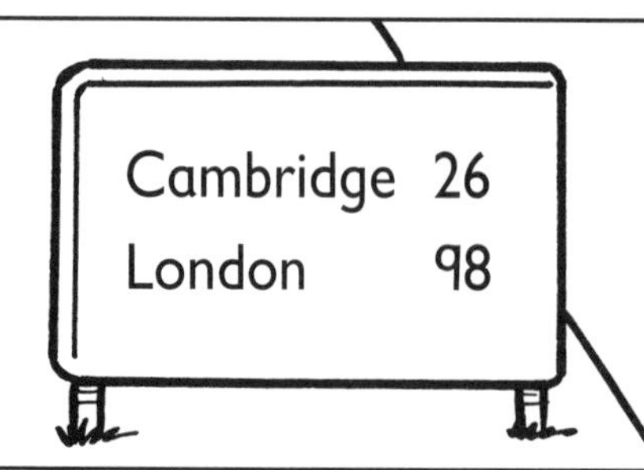

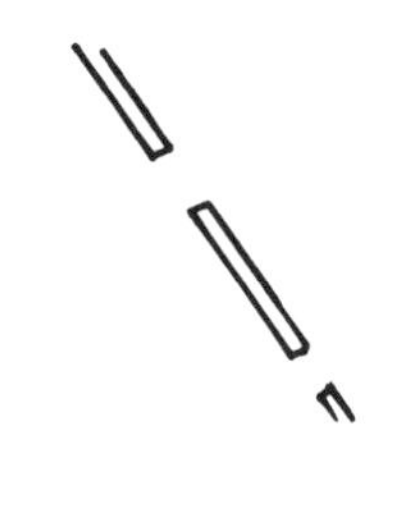

Whitby 48

3 If Jack drives one-quarter of the way to Whitby, how many more miles does he still have to drive?

_____ miles

4 Last week Jack drove to Manchester and back each weekday. How far did he drive in total?

_____ miles

Leeds 34
Oldham 67

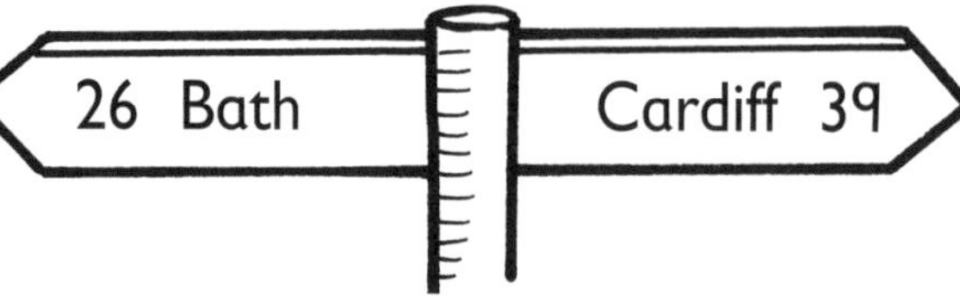

- **Use these signs to make up four questions for another pair to solve.**

Teachers' note Draw attention to the fact that different types of signposts work in different ways. For example when on a motorway, the signs show only the towns in one direction, whereas a two-armed signpost shows towns in two different directions. Talk about how this affects the operation used to solve the problem.

Post office problems

The mass of each parcel is shown.

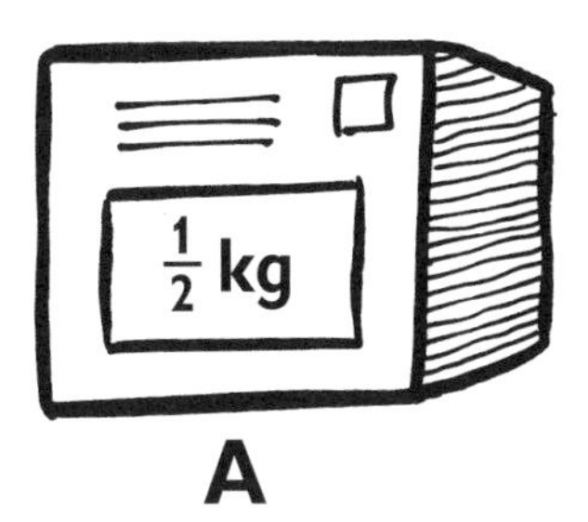

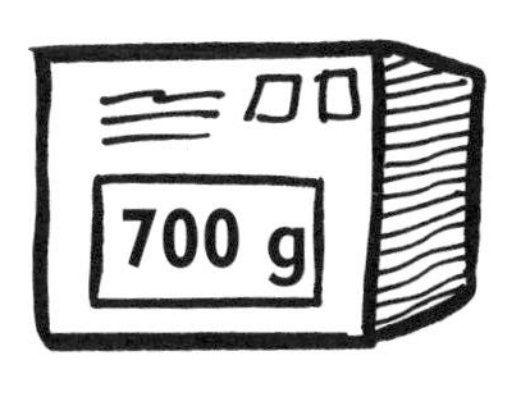

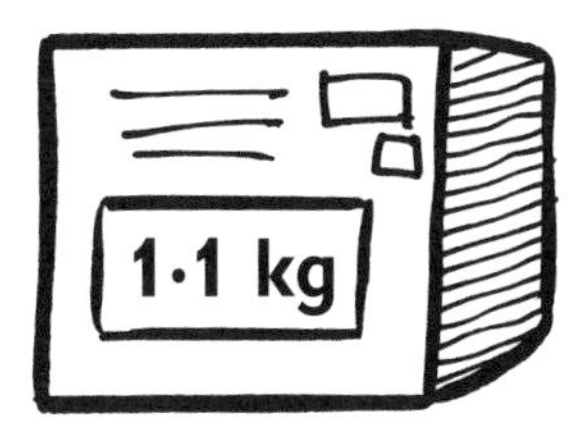

A B C D

1 Find the difference, in grams, between the heaviest and the lightest parcels. _____ g

2 Find the total mass, in kilograms, of the two heaviest parcels. _____ kg

3 Find the difference, in grams, between parcel A and parcel B. _____ g

4 In parcel D there is a pair of shoes. If the box itself weighs 100 g, how much does each shoe weigh? _____ g

5 Which three parcels together weigh 1.5 kg? ___ , ___ and ___

6 In parcel B there are three identical mugs. If the box itself weight 100 g, how much does each mug weigh? _____ g

7 In parcel A there are eight identical ornaments. If the box itself weighs 100 g, how much does each ornament weigh? _____ g

8 Find the total mass, in kilograms, of all four parcels. _____ kg

NOW TRY THIS!

- **Put the parcels into pairs so that one pair is exactly 1 kg heavier than the other pair.**

☐ and ☐ ☐ and ☐

Teachers' note Remind the children that 1000 g are equivalent to 1 kg, and revise equivalent masses of decimals to one decimal place, for example 0·7 kg or 1·3 kg. Ask the children to explain the strategies that they used to solve these problems.

Container problems: 1

- **Work out the answer to each question.**

Discuss your ideas with a partner.

Show your calculations on a separate piece of paper.

1

575 ml **150 ml** **?**

The total amount of liquid in these containers is 1 l. How much liquid is in the third container?

ml

2

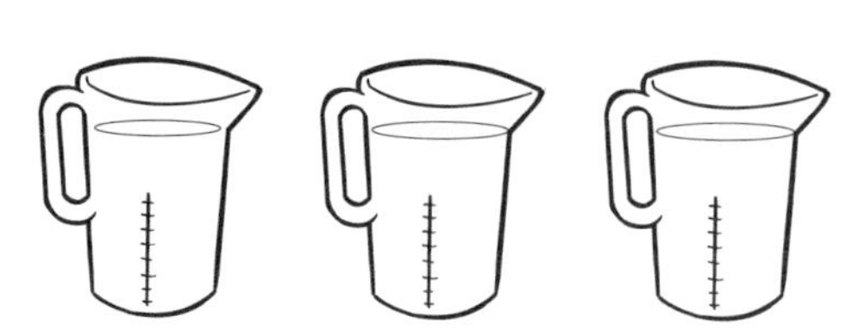

The total amount of liquid in these containers is 960 ml. Each holds the same amount. How much liquid is in each?

ml

3

375 ml **375 ml** **?**

The total amount of liquid in these containers is 2 l. How much liquid is in the largest container?

ml

4

?

Two identical containers together hold 750 ml. A smaller container holds 100 ml less than one of them. How much does it hold?

ml

5

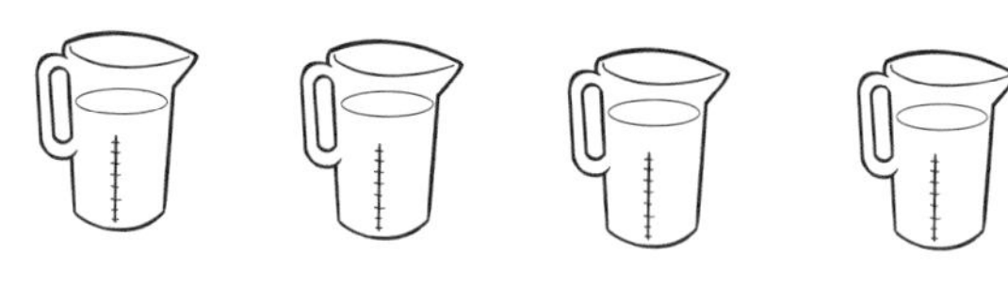

Four identical containers each hold 175 ml. What is the total amount of liquid in the containers?

ml

6

The larger container holds four times more than the smaller one. The smaller one holds 150 ml. What is the total amount of liquid in the containers?

ml

Teachers' note Use in conjunction with page 23, Container problems: 2. The whole worksheet can be given to the children to complete or, alternatively, the children could cut out the questions and use them as question cards, with different children in a group answering different questions. As an extension, ask the children to make up two container questions for a partner to solve.

Container problems: 2

- **Work out the answer to each question.**

Discuss your ideas with a partner.

Show your calculations on a separate piece of paper.

1

880 ml **?** **?**

The medium container holds half the amount of the large one. The smallest holds half the amount of the medium one. What is the total amount of liquid in the containers?

[ ] ml

2

? **?** **300 ml**

The total capacity of the containers is $2\frac{1}{2}$ l. Two hold the same amount and the smaller one holds 300 ml. What is the capacity of one of the larger containers?

[ ] ml

3

1600 ml **?** **?**

The total capacity of the containers is 3 l. Two have the same capacity and the larger one holds 1600 ml. What is the capacity of one of the smaller containers?

[ ] ml

4

460 ml **460 ml** **?**

Two identical containers each hold 460 ml. The larger container holds 240 ml more than one of them. What is the total capacity of the containers?

[ ] ml

5

720 ml **?**

The larger container holds three times more than the smaller one. The larger one holds 720 ml. What is the total capacity of the containers?

[ ] ml

6

90 ml **?**

The larger container holds four times more than the smaller one. The smaller one holds 90 ml. What is the capacity of the larger container?

[ ] ml

Teachers' note Use in conjunction with page 22, Container problems: 1. The whole worksheet can be given to the children to complete or, alternatively, the children could cut out the questions and use them as question cards, with different children in a group answering different questions. As an extension, ask the children to make up two container questions for a partner to solve.

Loopy witches

- ☆ Cut out the cards.
- ☆ Answer the 'start' card. Find the answer on one of the other cards, then answer that question.
- ☆ Put the cards in a loop on the table.

Start **6 l** Griselda has 180 ml. If she pours it equally into six bottles, how much is in each bottle? B	**3 l** Three blue tins each hold 300 ml and a red tin holds 600 ml. How much do the tins hold altogether? C
575 ml A bowl and a jug together hold 500 ml. If the bowl holds 100 ml more than the jug, how much does the bowl hold? M	**30 ml** A bucket holds 500 ml. If 150 ml is already in the bucket, how much more could it hold? R
$1\frac{1}{2}$ l If a jug holds $1\frac{1}{2}$ l, how much do four jugs hold? K	**300 ml** Griselda drank 450 ml more than Zelda. If Griselda drank 550 ml, how much did Zelda drink? S
350 ml A bowl holds 28 l. If the bowl holds seven times more than the kettle, how much does the kettle hold? O	**13 l** A bucket holds 6 l more than a pan. If these containers hold 12 l altogether, how much does the pan hold? I
100 ml If a bucket holds $6\frac{1}{2}$ l, how much do two buckets hold? T	**4 l** Gertrude drank 350 ml more than Maud. If Gertrude drank 225 ml, how much did Maud drink? O

Teachers' note As a quick way of checking the children's answers, use the letters at the bottom right of each card. If the cards are in the correct order they will spell a word (answer on page 63). Remind the children that 'ml' stands for 'millilitres' and 'l' stands for 'litres'.

Time teaser

☆ Work with a partner.

☆ Cut out the cards.

☆ Match a clock to each question card.

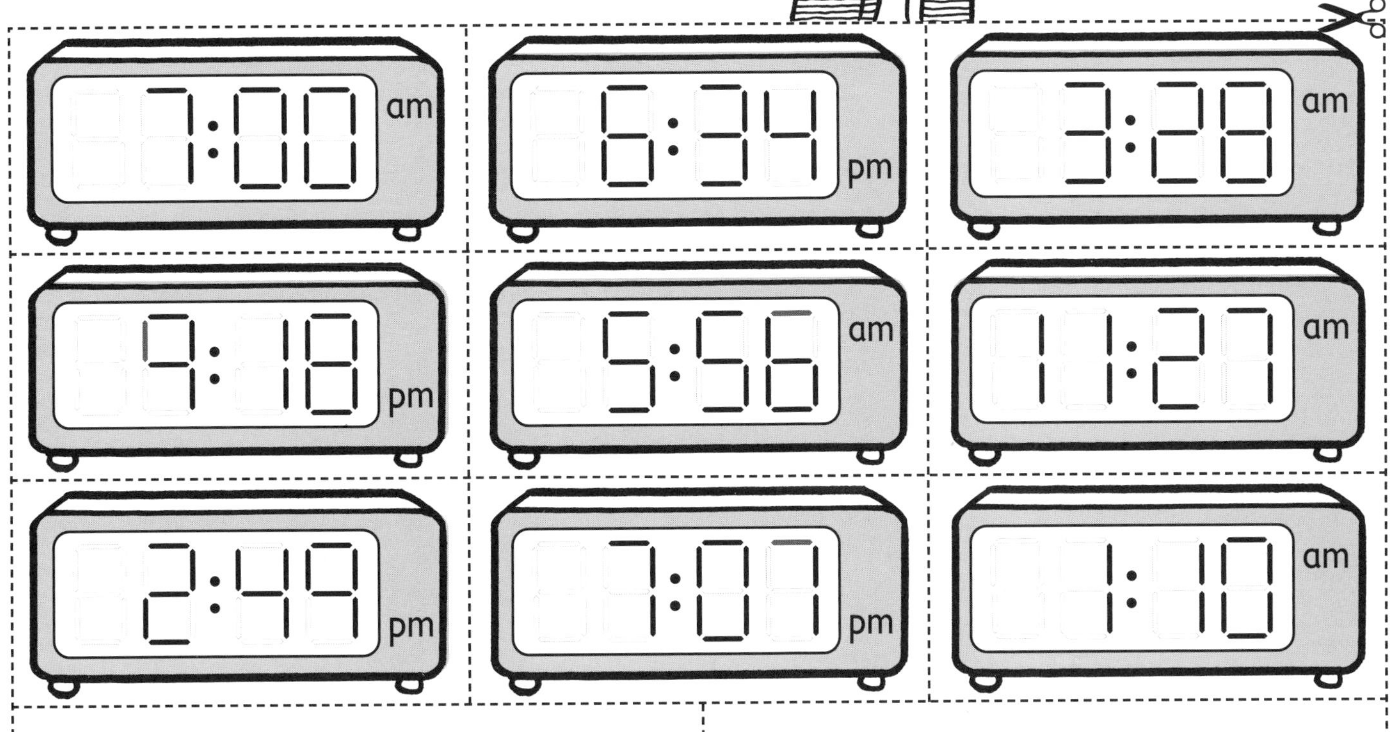

A Which of these times is nearest to twenty past six in the evening?

B Which of these times is nearest to ten past seven in the morning?

C Which of these times is between 1 o'clock and 3 o'clock in the afternoon?

D Which of these times shows four minutes to six in the morning?

E Which of these times is nearest to 8 o'clock in the evening?

F Which of these times is nearest to midnight?

G Which of these times is just before half past three in the morning?

H Which of these times comes next after nine-thirty in the morning?

Teachers' note As an extension, ask the children to write a question card for the remaining time, using vocabulary such as 'between', and saying whether the time is in the morning, afternoon or evening. Some children may benefit from having geared analogue clocks to help them with this activity.

Taxi!

- **Colour in the correct answer.**

1 I picked up a man at 4:27 pm and dropped him off at his home at 5:05 pm. How long was the journey?

44 mins	38 mins	32 mins

2 I picked up a woman at 6:48 am and dropped her off at her work 30 minutes later. What time did she arrive at work?

6:78am	7:18am	7:08am

3 The journey from the station to the town centre usually takes 26 minutes. Today it took one hour. How many minutes more is this?

44 mins	34 mins	24 mins

4 Each weekday I pick up a man at 7:56 am and drop him at work at 8:26 am. How many hours each week do I drive him?

$2\frac{1}{2}$ hours	150 hours	3 hours

5 I left home and drove for 35 minutes to a man's house. I arrived there at 12:07 pm. What time did I leave home?

11:42am	11:32am	12:42pm

6 I started driving at 11:25 pm. I took a break at 12:40 am. How long after I started was this?

$1\frac{1}{2}$ hours	$1\frac{1}{4}$ hours	25 mins

7 I started driving at 6:43 am. I took a break $2\frac{1}{2}$ hours later. What time was this?

8:23am	8:33am	9:13am

NOW TRY THIS!

- **Make up two taxi questions of your own for a partner to solve.**

Teachers' note The times can be altered to provide differentiation. Provide the children with geared analogue clocks to help them with this work, if necessary. Remind the children that there are 60 minutes in each hour.

Story-telling

- **Make up a story for each number sentence.**
- **Choose units from the box below to use in each story.**

kg g £ p mm cm m km ml l

1 $63 \div 9 = \square$

____

____

____

____

2 $45 - 12 + 8 = \square$

____

____

____

____

3 $9 \times 5 + 7 = \square$

____

____

____

____

4 $24 \div 8 + 7 = \square$

____

____

____

____

5 $60 \div \square = 12$

____

____

____

____

6 $10 \times 6 - \square = 42$

____

____

____

____

NOW TRY THIS!

- **On the back of this sheet, write the answer to each number sentence, giving the correct unit used in each story.**

Teachers' note You could alter the calculations to make them easier or more difficult, as appropriate, for different children. Children could continue their number stories on the back of the sheet if necessary. During the plenary, invite the children to read out their stories for others to listen to and to guess the calculation.

Calculator calamities: 1

These children have been making mistakes on the calculator.

- **Help them to correct their mistakes.**

1 Freya wanted to add 472 and 386.
She entered 172 + 386 by mistake.

Tick to show what she should press next to correct the mistake in one go.

- **+ 3** ☐
- **– 300** ☐
- **+ 300** ☐
- **– 386** ☐

2 Ben wanted to subtract 185 from 468.
He entered 468 – 85 by mistake.

Tick to show what he should press next to correct the mistake in one go.

- **+ 100** ☐
- **– 1** ☐
- **+ 185** ☐
- **– 100** ☐

3 Chloe wanted to add 489 to 392.
She entered 392 + 469 by mistake.

Tick to show what she should press next to correct the mistake in one go

- **+ 20** ☐
- **– 200** ☐
- **+ 2** ☐
- **– 20** ☐

4 Anoop wanted to take 384 from 927.
He entered 727 – 384 by mistake.

Tick to show what he should press next to correct the mistake in one go.

- **+ 2** ☐
- **– 200** ☐
- **+ 200** ☐
- **– 2** ☐

NOW TRY THIS!

- **Try this multiplication mistake.**

Daisy wanted to multiply 567 by 14.
She entered 567 × 13 by mistake.

Tick to show what she should press next to correct the mistake in one go.

- **× 1** ☐
- **+ 1** ☐
- **+ 567** ☐
- **× 567** ☐

Teachers' note Use in conjunction with page 29, Calculator calamities: 2, which can be used as further extension work and includes multiplication and division calculator mistakes to be undone. The numbers on this worksheet can be altered to provide differentiation.

Calculator calamities: 2

These children have been making mistakes on the calculator.

- **Help them to correct their mistakes.**

1 Sam wanted to multiply 12 by 34.
He entered 12 × 33 by mistake.

Tick to show what he should press next to correct the mistake in one go.

- **+ 1** ☐
- **× 1** ☐
- **+ 33** ☐
- **+ 12** ☐

2 Meena wanted to subtract 245 from 449.
She entered 449 – 205 by mistake.

Tick to show what she should press next to correct the mistake in one go.

- **+ 4** ☐
- **– 40** ☐
- **+ 40** ☐
- **– 205** ☐

3 Dan wanted to multiply 378 by 17.
He entered 378 × 18 by mistake.

Tick to show what he should press next to correct the mistake in one go.

- **+ 378** ☐
- **+ 1** ☐
- **– 378** ☐
- **– 1** ☐

4 Kimberley wanted to divide 368 by 4.
She entered 368 ÷ 2 by mistake.

Tick to show what she should press next to correct the mistake in one go.

- **× 2** ☐
- **+ 2** ☐
- **÷ 2** ☐
- **– 2** ☐

- **Try this division mistake.**

David wanted to divide 252 by 3.
He entered 252 ÷ 6 by mistake.

Tick to show what he should press next to correct the mistake in one go.

- **÷ 2** ☐
- **× 2** ☐
- **÷ 3** ☐
- **× 3** ☐

Teachers' note Use in conjunction with page 28, Calculator calamities: 1, which can be used as an introductory worksheet. The numbers on this worksheet can be altered to provide differentiation.

Quiz show

- **For each question, colour the correct calculation.**

1

A piece of string 108 cm long is cut into four equal pieces. How can you find the length of each piece?

A 108 + 4 **B** 108 × 4
C 108 – 4 **D** 108 ÷ 4

2

It takes Joe six minutes to wash a car. How can you find how many minutes it will take him to wash three cars?

A 6 + 3 **B** 6 × 3
C 6 – 3 **D** 6 ÷ 3

3

Kay has 560 ml of milkshake. She drinks 80 ml of it. How can you find how much she has left?

A 560 + 80 **B** 560 × 80
C 560 – 80 **D** 560 ÷ 80

4

Leo needs £42. He saves £3 each week. How can you find how many weeks it will take him to save the money?

A 42 + 3 **B** 42 × 3
C 42 – 3 **D** 42 ÷ 3

5

Thirty-two people live on a street. Four people live in each house. How can you find how many houses there are?

A 32 + 4 **B** 32 × 4
C 32 – 4 **D** 32 ÷ 4

6

It is 25 miles from Olby to Raw, and 17 miles from Weld to Raw. How can you find how far it is from Olby to Weld, via Raw?

A 25 + 17 **B** 25 × 17
C 25 – 17 **D** 25 ÷ 17

NOW TRY THIS!

- **On the back of this sheet, write a question to match each of these calculations.**

A 35 + 27 **B** 26 × 5
C 56 – 35 **D** 126 ÷ 3

Teachers' note The numbers can be altered to provide differentiation. Encourage the children to write each question as a calculation and to describe their strategy for working out each answer, including showing this on a number line, using a written method, or on a 100-square.

Number sentences

- **Colour to show which number sentences could be used for each situation.**

1 James is nine years old. His father is 32 years old. How many years younger is James than his father?

A 9 + □ = 32	**B** 32 – □ = 9	**C** 32 – 9 = □

2 Sam's mum gives him 45 stickers to add to his collection and his dad gives him 38 stickers. If Sam now has 100 stickers, how many did he have to begin with?

A □ + 45 + 38 = 100	**B** 100 – 45 – 38 = □	**C** 45 + 38 – 100 = □

3 Chloe's photo album holds four photos per page. The album has eight pages. Chloe fills the album, but then takes out two photos. How many photos are in the album?

A □ + 4 × 8 = 2	**B** 4 × 8 – □ = 2	**C** 8 × 4 – 2 = □

4 After spending 78p and £1.36, Sara has 37p left. How much did she have to begin with?

A □ – 78 – 136 = 37	**B** 78 + 136 – 37 = □	**C** 78 + 136 + 37 = □

NOW TRY THIS!

- **On the back of this sheet, write number sentences to match this problem.**

Juggling balls come in bags of three. How many bags does Clive buy so that his six children can have four balls each?

Teachers' note Remind the children that the focus here is not on solving the problem, but on deciding which number sentences could represent the situation. Explain that several different number sentences could be used for each. Encourage the children to describe their reasoning and to make up problems like these of their own.

Café life

- **Write number sentences to work out these problems.**

1 The café opens a box of 500 straws. If 20 are used each week, for how many weeks will the straws last?

$500 \div 20 = 25$

2 If a quarter of the 32 chairs in the café have arms, how many chairs do **not** have arms?

3 A cake costs £4.50 to make. It is cut into eight slices, and each slice sold for £1.25. How much profit is made?

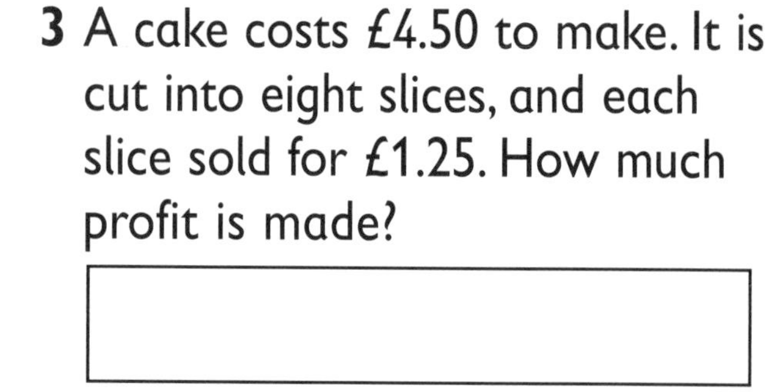

4 A customer buys a £1.69 coffee, a 70p sausage roll and a £1.25 slice of cake. How much does he spend?

5 A milkshake is one-fifth of a litre. How many millilitres are needed to make three milkshakes?

6 A large coffee is 78p more than a small coffee. A large coffee costs £1.69. How much does a small coffee cost?

7 A customer has £5. How many 55p iced buns can she buy?

- **Write a café question to match this number sentence:**

187 + 65 = ?

Teachers' note Note that different calculations could be written for each question. Ask the children to show how they might solve each question on a number line or 100-square. Encourage them to describe the strategies they used and to compare differences in the calculations suggested for each question, for example □ + 78 = 169 or 169 – 78 = □.

Billy the Baker's cakes

- **Cut out the number cards and place them in the boxes.**
- **How many different questions and answers can you make?**

Billy the Baker has ☐ trays of iced buns

and ☐ trays of cream puffs.

There are ☐ iced buns on each tray

and ☐ cream puffs on each tray.

How many cakes are there altogether?

- **Write your questions and answers here.**

5	6	3	8	4

Teachers' note Remind the children that they can write calculations and answers on the back of the worksheet too. Encourage them to work systematically so that they can tell whether they have generated all the possible different questions. As an extension, ask them to work out how many more answers they could make if they also had a '7' card.

How?

- **Show how each child could have worked out the answer.**

1 Jen worked out the correct answer to 16×5.
Her answer was 80.

2 Alfie worked out the correct answer to $90 \div 5$.
His answer was 18.

3 Harry worked out the correct answer to $360 \div 3$.
His answer was 120.

4 Hannah worked out the correct answer to 24×8.
Her answer was 192.

- **Talk to a partner about which question you found the hardest.**

Teachers' note It is important that children are given the opportunity to consider different ways that answers to calculations could be found, including drawing, using practical material, number lines, 100-squares, place value cards, etc. Compare the children's completed worksheets and encourage them to say which methods they think are most useful or easy to work with.

Measuring methods

- **Show how each question could be answered.**

1 How many bottles, each holding a quarter of a litre, can be filled from a bucket holding $5\frac{1}{2}$ l?

2 I have three-quarters of a kilogram of flour. If I use 50 g each day, how many days will it take me to use all the flour?

3 Jo walks 125 m from her house to the bus stop and then back again each day. How many days will it take her to walk $3\frac{1}{2}$ km?

4 It takes a quarter of an hour for a train to travel 25 miles. At this speed, how far would it travel in two hours?

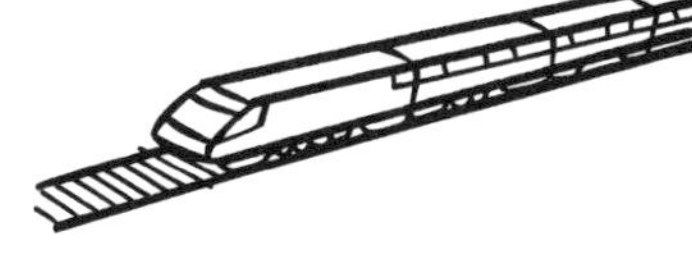

- **How much less than 3 m is the total of these lengths? ____ cm**

$\frac{3}{4}$ m   75 cm   100 mm   0·6 m

Teachers' note Revise the equivalents of units of measurement, such as 10 mm = 1 cm, 100 cm = 1 m, 1000 m = 1 km, 1000 g = 1 kg and 1000 ml = 1 l. Discuss halves and quarters of whole large units, for example $\frac{1}{2}$ kg or $\frac{1}{4}$ l.

Coin contest

Jo can use any <u>four</u> coins. Sam can use any <u>six</u> coins.

We must always use exactly this number of coins.

- Tick to show who you <u>think</u> can make the most amounts between 20p and 50p.

Jo Sam

- Which amounts between 20p and 50p can one of them make that the other cannot?

Show your workings here.

NOW TRY THIS!

- Design a leaflet or poster to show what you found out.

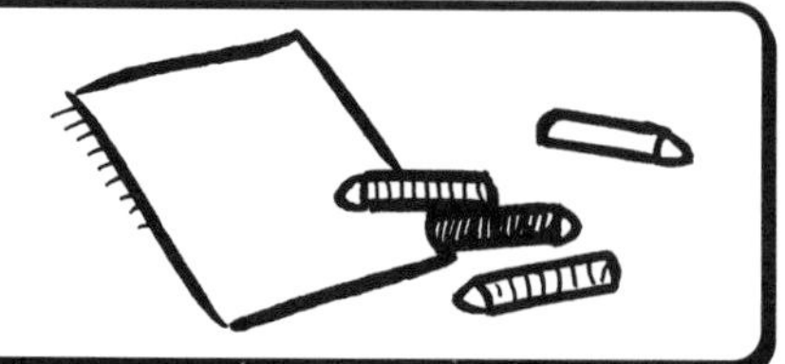

Teachers' note The numbers can be altered to provide differentiation, for example between 6p and 60p, or between 30p and 40p. Encourage the children to work systematically and to show their findings in a clear way so that others can understand them easily, for example using a table or diagrams.

Sour grapes

There are many ways in which Jack can eat these six grapes. Here are just a few ways:

One grape at a time	Two grapes, then four grapes	Even six grapes at once!
1 + 1 + 1 + 1 + 1 + 1	2 + 4	6

- **Find all the different ways of eating one, two, three, four, five and six grapes.**

Number of grapes	Different ways	Total number of ways
1		
2		
3		
4		
5		
6		

Teachers' note Encourage the children to work systematically and to be convinced that there are no solutions that they have missed. If all the solutions are found, the children should be able to see patterns in the numbers (see pages 63 and 64). As an extension, ask the children to predict the number of ways for seven and eight grapes, and to explain their thinking to a partner.

Field event

In a field, one-quarter **of the animals are horses.**

One-third **of the animals are cows.**

There are also 10 **sheep.**

- **How many: a** horses are there ? ____ **b** cows are there ? ____

  c animals are there altogether? ____

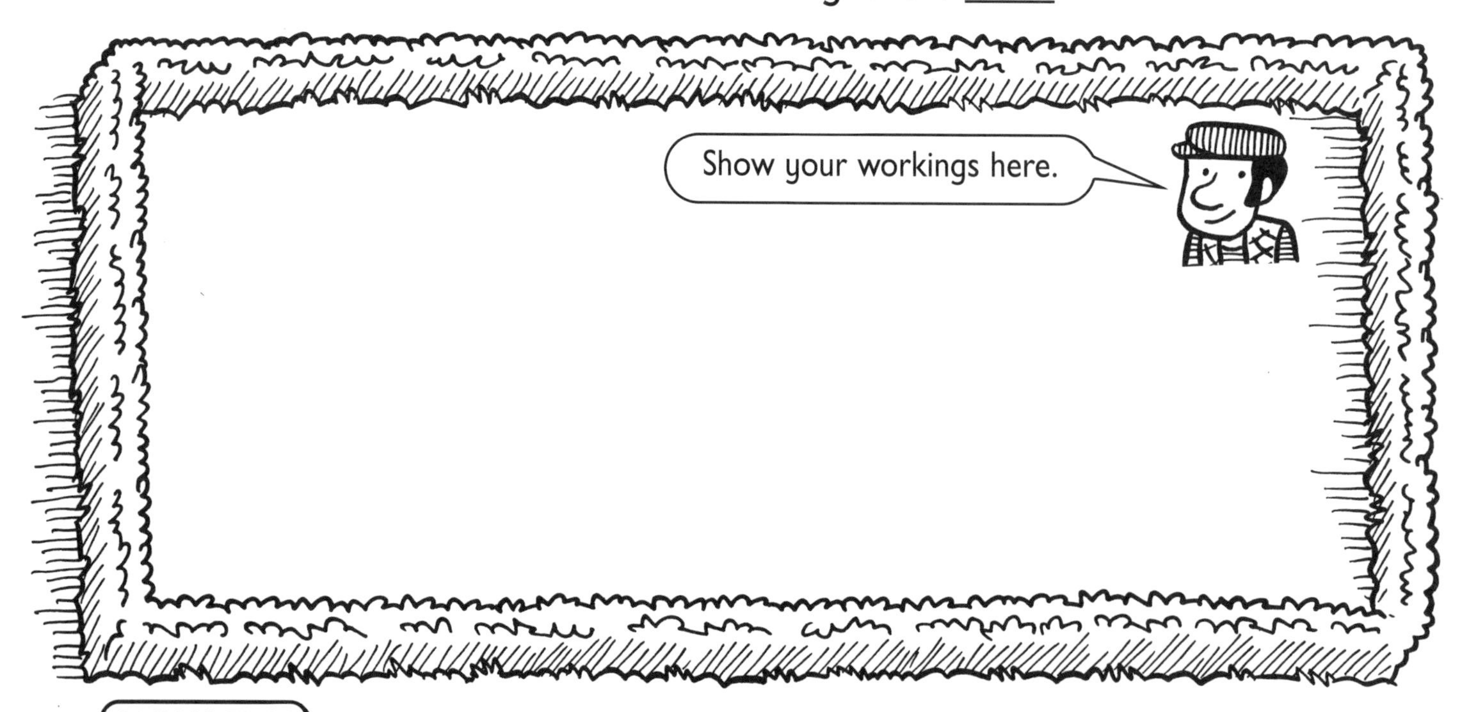

- **Write any multiple of 5 (except 10) into the empty box and solve the problem.**

In a field, one-quarter **of the animals are horses.**

One-third **of the animals are cows.**

There are also ☐ **sheep.**

- **How many: a** horses are there ? ____ **b** cows are there ? ____

  c animals are there altogether? ____

Teachers' note Encourage the children to create a range of new questions of this type and to explain how each question could be solved. More confident children could explore solutions where one-eighth of the animals are horses and where the number of sheep is any multiple of 10.

Tent teaser

- **Use the clues to help you work out the total number of children at the camp.**

Work with a partner.

In tent D there are four children. 

Three of the tents have the same number of children. 

Tent C has the most children sleeping in it.
It has two more children than any other tent. 

In Tent A there are two fewer children than in tent B.  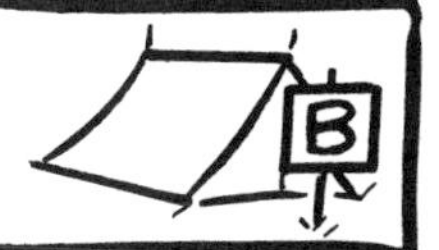

The total number of children in tent A and tent B is 10. 

- **How many children are at the camp altogether?** 

NOW TRY THIS!

- **Draw five tents of your own and decide how many children are in each tent.**
- **Make up clues for your partner to solve.**

Teachers' note If children are struggling with this activity, provide further clues. When completing the extension activity, encourage the children to check whether they have given a clue for each tent, without saying how many are in most of the tents. Display phrases like 'more than', 'fewer than', 'the most', the fewest' and 'the same number' to help the children make up their own clues.

Sheep and goats

- **Look at this fact:**

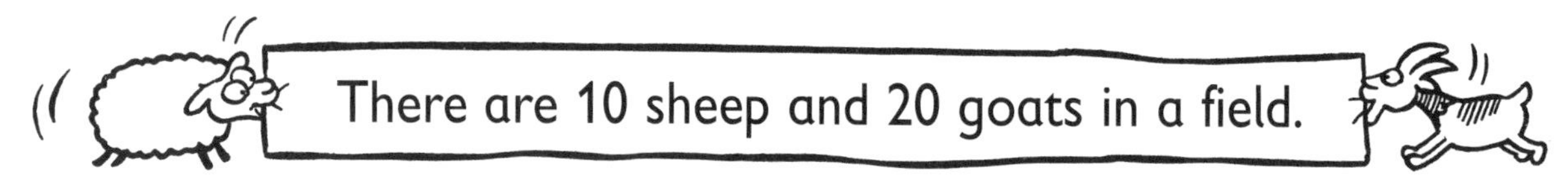

- **Tick to show whether each statement is true or false.**
- **Use words or pictures to explain to a partner why.**

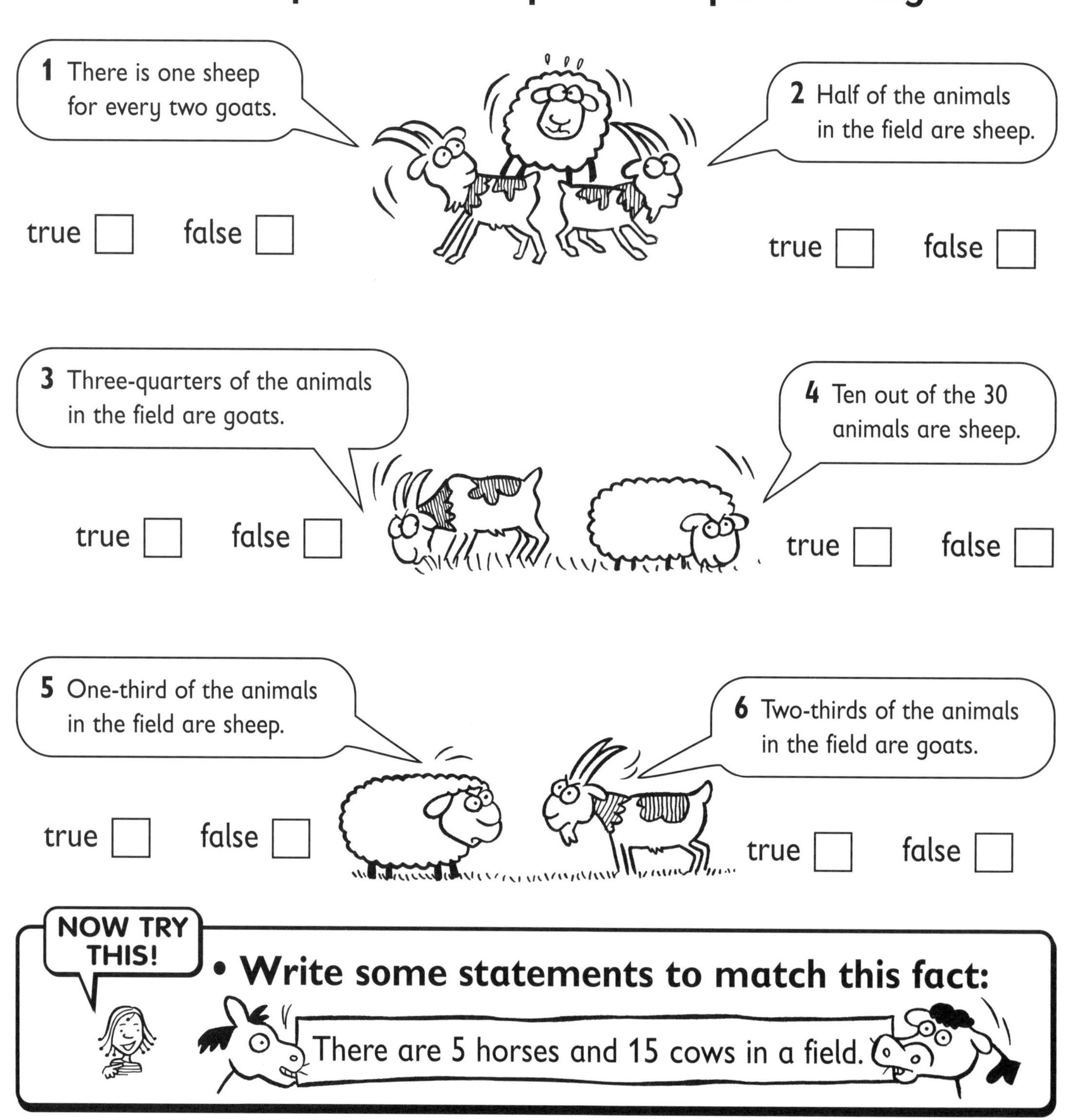

Teachers' note It is important that the children are given an opportunity to explain their thinking for each of these statements. They could explain in words, to the class, or draw diagrams that can illustrate the relationship between the number of sheep and goats. The children will need extra paper for this activity.

Fruit segments

There are 24 children.

Each child eats the same amount of fruit.

There are four apples and six satsumas.

Each apple can be cut into halves or quarters.

Each satsuma has 12 segments.

- **Write four questions about the information above for a partner to answer. You could start your questions with:**

How many ..?

What is the most ..?

What is the fewest ..?

If all the apples are shared ..?

If four satsumas are shared ..?

How many segments ..?

What fraction of the apples ..?

1 ______________________________

____

2 ______________________________

____

3 ______________________________

____

4 ______________________________

____

NOW TRY THIS!

- **Swap worksheets with your partner and answer his/her questions.**

Teachers' note This activity encourages the children to make up their own questions using appropriate vocabulary. When the children exchange worksheets for the extension activity, encourage them to describe how they decided what to do and to use number sentences to show the operation used. The numbers could be altered to provide differentiation.

Thinking thimbles

Li collects thimbles and wants to display some on a shelf with three sections. In each section she could put no thimbles, one thimble or two thimbles.

- How many different ways do you think Li could do this?
- Draw the thimbles to show the ways.

NOW TRY THIS!

Li keeps three gold thimbles on a special 3-section shelf. Each section can hold up to three thimbles.

- What arrangements are possible?

Teachers' note Ensure the children understand that a 0, 1, 2 shelf is the same as a 2, 1, 0 shelf, just with the shelves in different places. Discuss alternative ways of recording solutions to the extension activity, for example 012, 222, 121. Some children may, however, prefer to have a second blank sheet, or squared paper, on which to record the solutions.

Book counting

- **Names of the children in our group.**

Work in a group of three or four.

______________________ ______________________

______________________ ______________________

- **How many books are there in our school library?**

We estimate that there are about ______ books.

- **How are we going to find out?**

____

____

____

- **What information do we need?**

____

____

____

- **What do we think we will find, and why?**

____

____

____

- **How will we find the information?**

____

____

____

Teachers' note This activity should be done in small groups. The children should plan how they would go about answering the question. The focus should be on planning the investigation, and time should be spent discussing all the children's work.

Planning enquiries: 1

- **Work with a partner.**
- **Read through the questions and choose one question to work with.**

You need Planning enquiries: 2.

Is it true that the height of the school is more than six metres?

Is it true that fewer than half of the children in our class like cauliflower?

It is true that most of the children in our class have more than six letters in their first name?

Is it true that more than one-third of the children in our class have had chickenpox?

Is it true that the teachers in our school drink more coffee than tea?

Is it true that three-quarters of the children in our class are in bed by 9 o'clock?

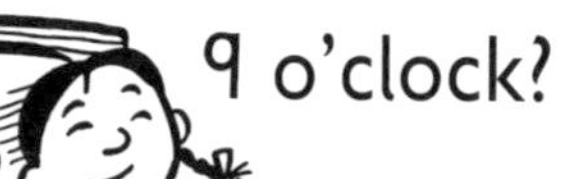

- **Cut out your chosen question and stick it onto Planning enquiries: 2**

Teachers' note Use in conjunction with page 45, Planning enquiries: 2. Working in pairs, the children should choose a question and then stick it onto the following worksheet. They should then plan how they would go about answering the question. The focus should be on planning the investigation, and time should be spent discussing all the children's work.

Planning enquiries: 2

- **Our names:**

____

____

Stick your chosen question here.

- **Show how you could find out whether your statement is true.**

1 What information do we want to collect?	2 How are we going to collect the information?
______________________	______________________
3 What equipment do we need, or what do we need to prepare before collecting the information?	4 What do you think the information will tell us, and why?
______________________	______________________

Teachers' note Use in conjunction with page 44, Planning enquiries: 1. As an extension, ask the children to discuss any problems that they think they might encounter.

Confetti colours

- **Use the clues to help you colour each pattern in the correct way.**

Work with a partner.

1

Blue is not next to yellow.
One heart is yellow.
Red is between pink and blue.
Both stars are the same colour.
Green is under blue.

2

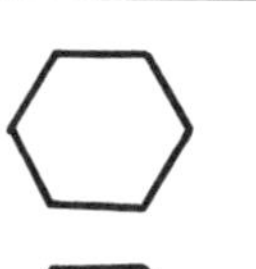

Green is not next to blue.
Three shapes are blue.
One hexagon is orange.
Red is under blue.
Orange is to the left of blue.

3

No heart is red.
Red is between pink and blue.
Both stars are the same colour.
Green is not next to red.
Pink is not next to green.
Yellow is above red.

4

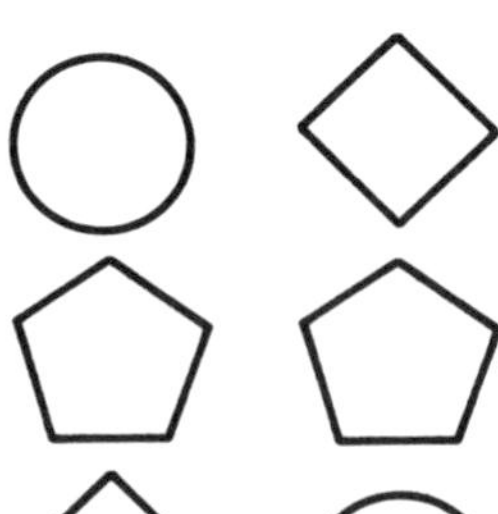

Blue is between yellow and red.
Both circles are the same colour.
Orange is to the right of blue.
Yellow is under orange.
There are two red shapes.

NOW TRY THIS!

- **Make up some confetti colour puzzles of your own for a partner to solve.**

Teachers' note Ask the children to work in pairs to solve these puzzles and provide them with a range of coloured pencils. Before colouring their final solutions they should be encouraged to check that each clue works.

Shelf stacking

- **Cut out the cards. Your teacher will give you clues to help you place the objects correctly on the shelves.**

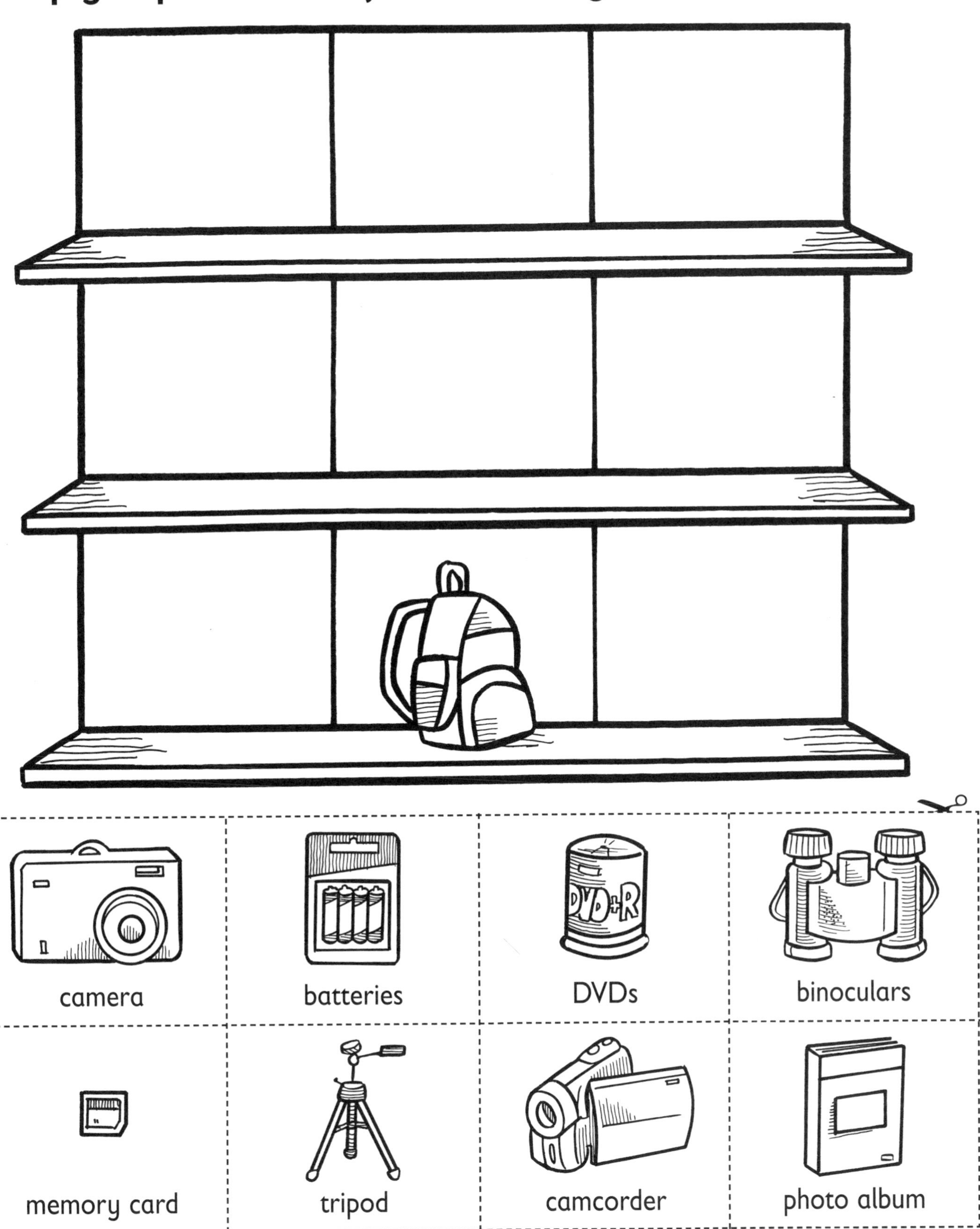

Teachers' note Use in conjunction with page 48, Shelf stacking clues, which provides three different sets of clues as to how the objects should be positioned, from an easy level through to a hard level. The solutions for the three sets of clues are different from each other so that the children can try each of the activities, using the same pieces.

Shelf stacking clues

Set 1

- The tripod is on the bottom shelf.
- Above the rucksack is the camera.
- The camera is between the memory card and the DVDs.
- The DVDs are to the left of the camera.
- Above the memory card are the batteries.
- The binoculars are to the right of the rucksack.
- The photo album is between the camcorder and the batteries.

Set 2

- The camcorder is above the batteries.
- The binoculars are on the top shelf.
- To the right of the rucksack is the tripod.
- The memory card is between the rucksack and the binoculars.
- The camera is on the bottom shelf.
- Between the camera and the photo album are the DVDs.

Set 3

- The memory card is **not** to the left of the rucksack.
- The camcorder and the camera are on the middle shelf.
- Above the camera is the tripod.
- The tripod is to the right of the DVDs.
- Between the DVDs and the rucksack is the photo album.
- Neither the batteries nor the memory card are on the top shelf.

Teachers' note Use in conjunction with page 47, Shelf stacking.

The rules of the rows

- **Fill in the missing numbers to match these rules.**

☆ The square is always five more than the triangle in the same row.

☆ The circle is always double the triangle in the same row.

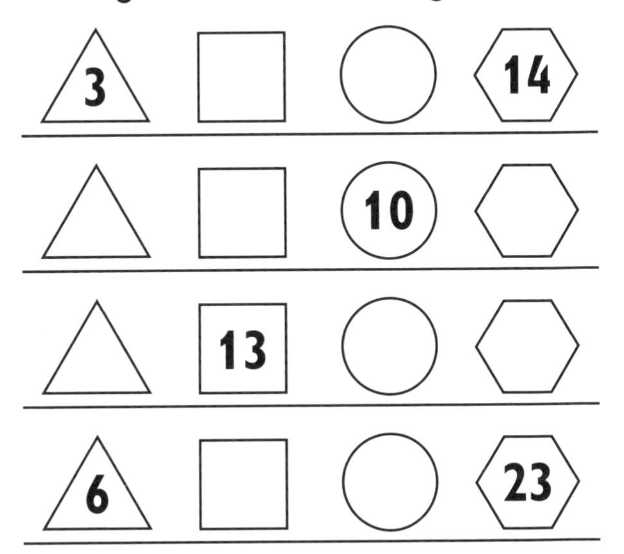

- **What is the rule for the hexagon?**

Explain it to a partner.

NOW TRY THIS!

- **Fill in the missing numbers to match these rules.**

☆ The triangle is always half the square in the same row.

☆ The circle is always the sum of the triangle and the square in the same row.

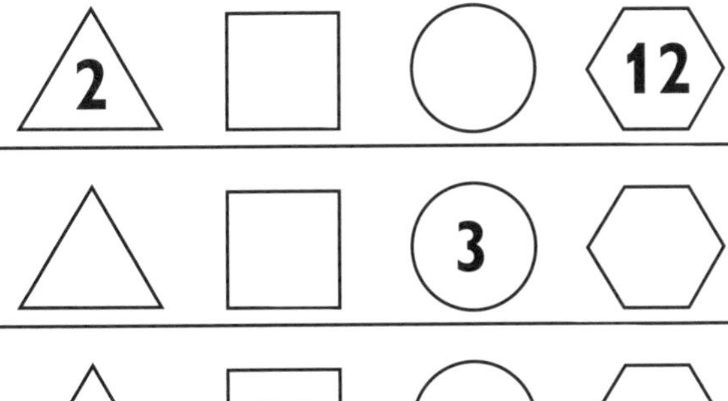

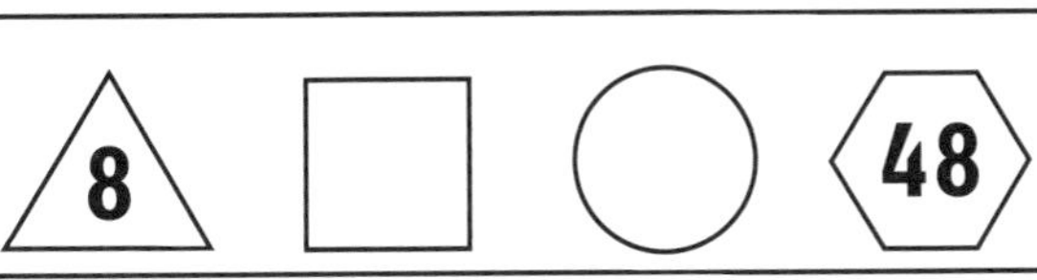

- **Can you find different rules for the hexagon?**

Teachers' note Encourage the children to look for relationships in the completed grids, for example writing a new rule to compare the triangle and circle numbers or the triangle and hexagon numbers of the second grid. The children could also make up their own rules and devise puzzles for a partner to solve.

Necklace numbers

- **Fill in the missing numbers in these necklace sequences.**

1 17, 20, 23, ___, ___, ___, ___, ___, ___

2 ___, 13, 17, 21, ___, ___, ___, ___, ___

3 ___, ___, ___, 18, 23, 28, ___, ___, ___

4 ___, ___, ___, 19, 25, 31, ___, ___, ___

5 ___, 7, ___, 17, 22, ___, ___, ___, ___

6 ___, ___, 8, ___, 14, ___, 20, ___, ___

7 ___, ___, ___, ___, ___, ___, 46, 50, 54

8 ___, ___, ___, ___, 29, ___, 41, ___, 53

- **Discuss the rule for each sequence with a partner.**

NOW TRY THIS!

- **Make up your own necklace sequence for a partner to solve.**

Teachers' note Encourage the children to find the difference between adjacent numbers in each sequence where possible, and then to extend the sequences in the directions necessary. Where there are no adjacent numbers, the children can find the difference between given numbers and halve the answer to find the intermediate number.

Sticks

Ali and Sally have been making shapes using sticks of different lengths.

- **Use the clues below to work out which shapes each child made.**
- **Colour Ali's shapes red, and Sally's shapes blue.**

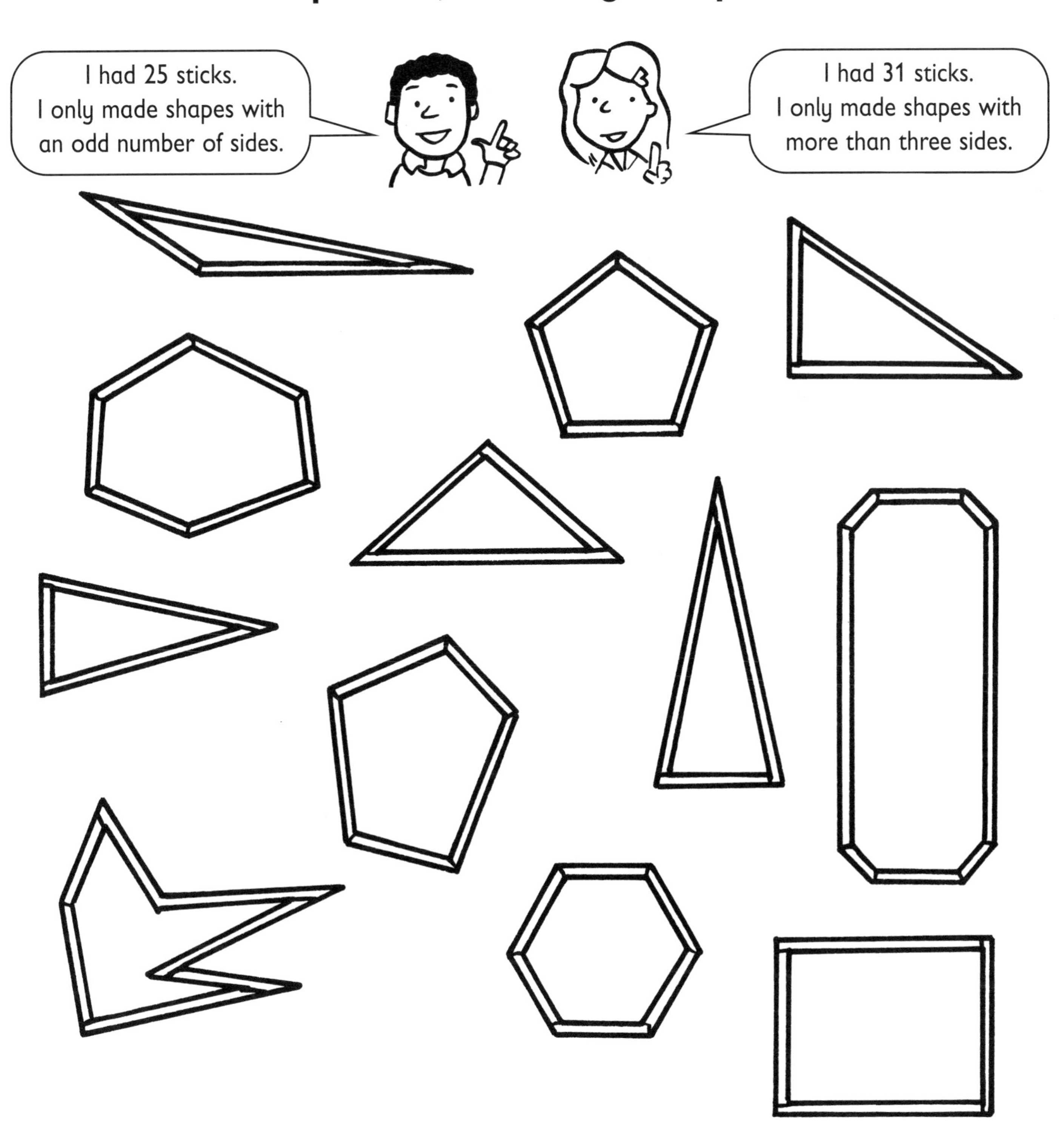

Teachers' note Ensure the children understand that when a rule applies to one person it does not necessarily mean that the opposite is true for the other person, for example because Ali only makes shapes with an odd number of sides, it does **not** mean that Sally only makes shapes with an even number of sides.

Tell me

☆ Work with a partner.

☆ Cut out the cards and place them face down in a pile.

☆ Take turns to pick a card and describe the shapes on the card so that your partner can draw them exactly onto a piece of paper.

Don't let your partner see the shapes!

☆ Use these words to help you.

equilateral isosceles right angle halfway along
length width edge vertex in the middle
horizontal vertical diagonal inside underneath

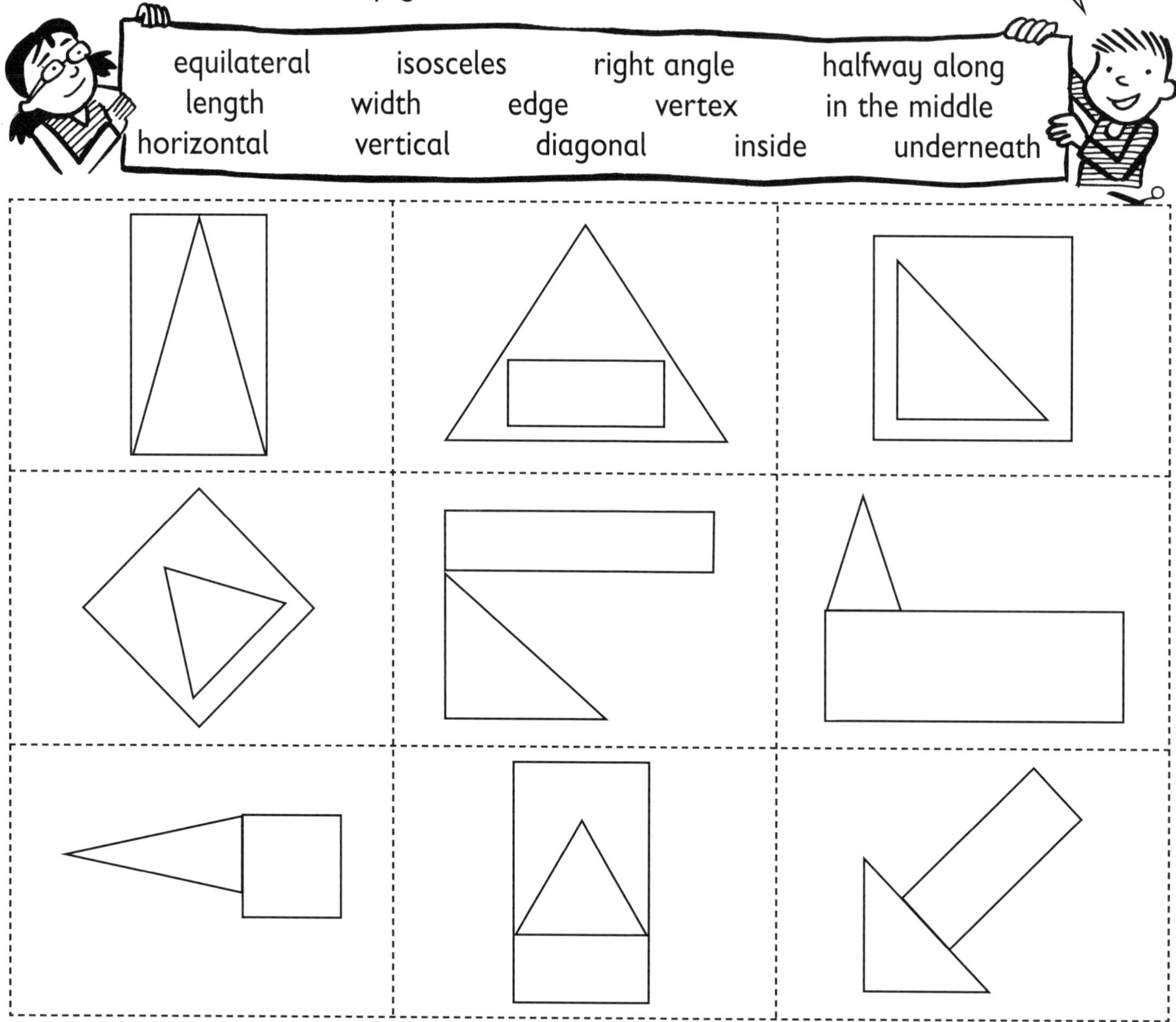

NOW TRY THIS!

- **Write descriptions of three of the cards so that someone else could pick them from this set.**

Teachers' note Ideally, this worksheet should be copied onto card so that the shapes cannot be seen through the paper. As a further extension, encourage the children to talk to each other about the shapes and to decide how they would like to sort them into groups. Accept any ways of sorting, encouraging the children to explain their reasoning to others.

True statements

- ☆ Cut out the cards.
- ☆ How many true statements can you make using the cards?
- ☆ You do not have to use all the cards in a statement.
- ☆ Record your answers below.

6 is a factor of 54

is a factor of				is the product of
multiplied by				is a multiple of
6	9	54	=	divided by

Teachers' note The numbers can be altered to provide differentiation. Encourage the children to work systematically to find all the possible solutions. As an extension, the children could record all possible number sentences that can be made with those numbers.

Dividing exactly

- **Which number from this board is each child talking about?**
- **Write it in the box.**

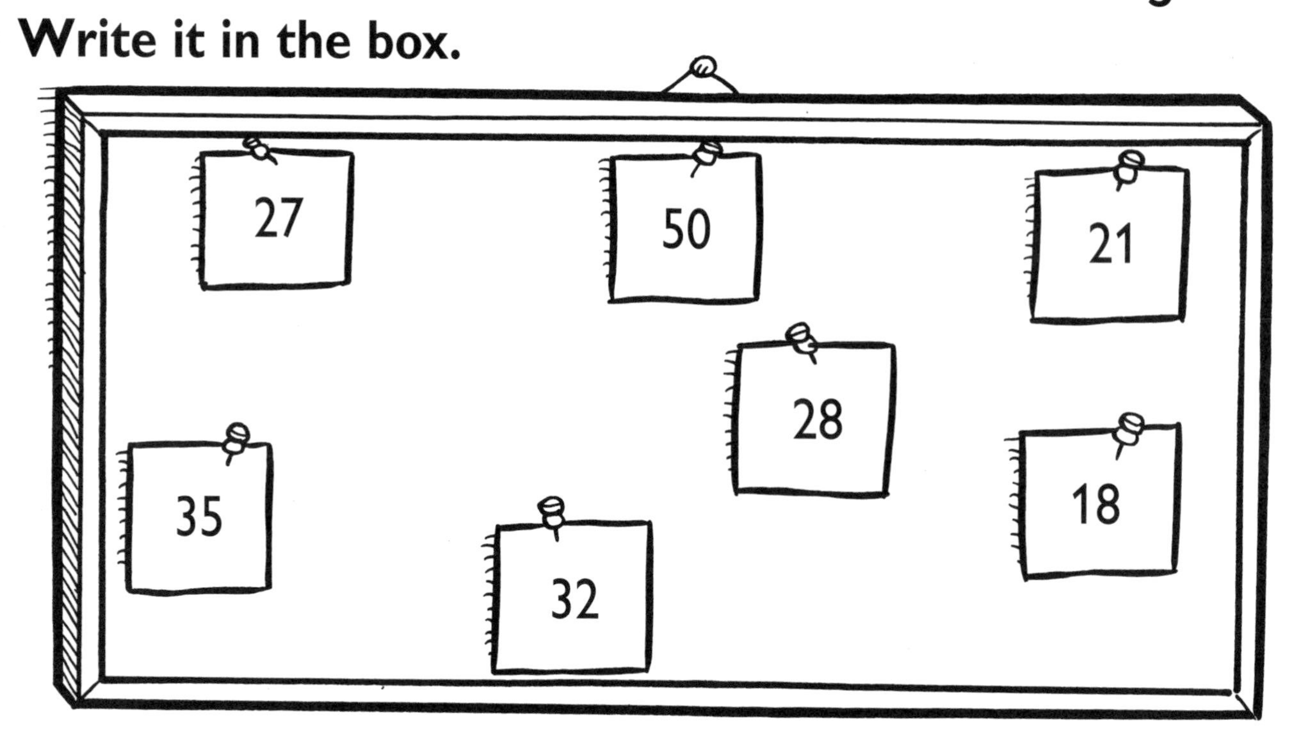

My number divides exactly by 2, by 5 and by 10.

☐ Hussain

My number divides exactly by 3, but **not** by 6 or by 9.

☐ Jane

My number divides exactly by 2 and by 4, but **not** by 8.

☐ Jermaine

My number divides exactly by 9 and by 3, but **not** by 6.

☐ Benny

My number divides exactly by 5, but **not** by 10.

☐ Jenny

My number divides exactly by 2, by 3 and by 6.

☐ Penny

NOW TRY THIS!

- **Which of the numbers is not described?** ____
- **Write all the numbers that divide exactly into it.**

____

Teachers' note The numbers can be altered to provide differentation. Encourage the children to discuss the nature of different multiples of a number, for example that multiples of 10 end in zero, and to write their own descriptions about other numbers given.

Halfway house

- **Colour true or false for each statement.**
- **Write examples on the houses to prove it.**

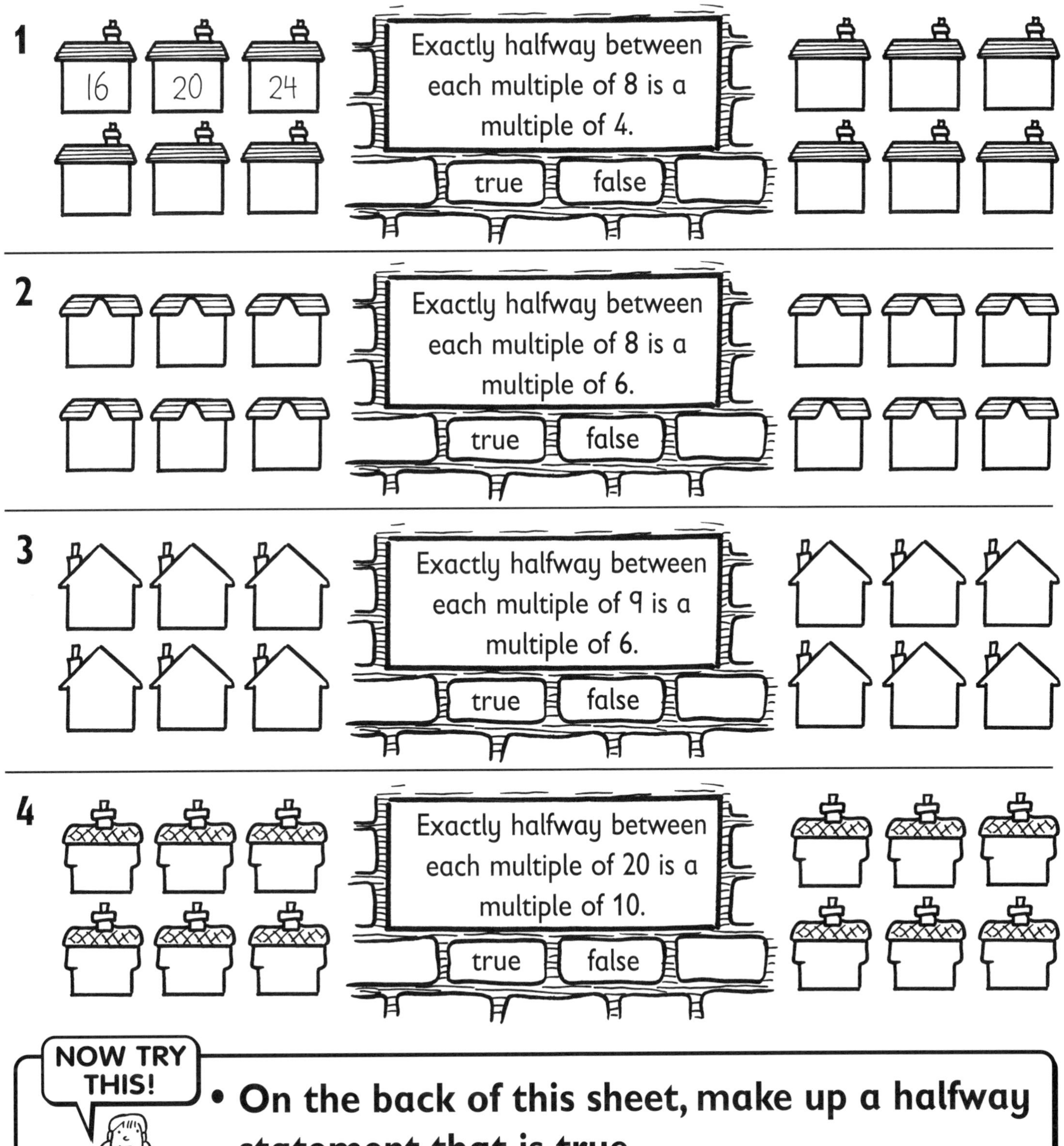

NOW TRY THIS!

- **On the back of this sheet, make up a halfway statement that is true.**
- **Write four examples to prove it.**

Teachers' note Remind the children of the meaning of the word 'multiples' and identify some on a number line. Emphasise that the halfway number must be exactly halfway, and demonstrate this on a number line if necessary. Ensure the children understand that giving one example is insufficient to prove a general statement, although one example can be enough to disprove it.

Hard cards

☆ Cut out the cards and turn them face down.

☆ Take turns to pick a card and answer the question.

☆ Ask your partner to check your answer.

Work with a partner.

1

The numbers on these cards are both **odd**. If I add them together, will the answer be odd or even?

______

2

One of these cards is **odd**. One is **even**. If I find the difference between them, will the answer be odd or even?

______

3

One of these cards is **odd**. One is **even**. If I add them together, will the answer be odd or even?

______

4

The numbers on these cards are both **odd**. If I multiply them together, will the answer be odd or even?

______

5

If I double the number on this card, will the answer be odd or even?

______

6

The numbers on these three cards are all **odd**. If I add them together, will the answer be odd or even?

______

7

If I multiply the number on this card by four, will the answer be odd or even?

______

8

The numbers on these cards are both **even**. If I add them together, will the answer be odd or even?

______

9

The numbers on these four cards are all **odd**. If I add them together, will the answer be odd or even?

______

10

One of these cards is **odd**. The other is **even**. If I find the product of them, will the answer be odd or even?

______

Teachers' note If necessary, remind the children how to recognise odd and even numbers before they begin this activity. The children could be given sets of number cards, from 1–9 or 1–100, to help them realise that these general statements apply to all sizes of numbers. As an extension, ask the children to write four examples on the back of each card to prove the answer.

Number puzzles

Each grid shows part of a number square.
Some numbers are shaded to form a sequence.
- **Write the rule for each sequence.**

1

95	96	97	98
105	106	107	108
115	116	117	118
125	126	127	128

____

2

56	57	58	59
66	67	68	69
76	77	78	79
86	87	88	89

____

3

102	103	104	105
112	113	114	115
122	123	124	125
132	133	134	135

____

4

84	85	86	87	88	89
94	95	96	97	98	99
104	105	106	107	108	109
114	115	116	117	118	119

____

5

171	172	173	174	175	176
181	182	183	184	185	186
191	192	193	194	195	196

____

6

134	135	136	137
144	145	146	147
154	155	156	157
164	165	166	167

____

Teachers' note Explain how rules for sequences can be written, for example 'adding 10' or 'counting on in tens'. Encourage the children to discuss each sequence with a partner and to look at the different ways of describing each rule. As an extension, ask the children to make up their own number grid puzzle for a partner to solve.

3 for 2!

- **For each question, tick to show which is the better offer and work out how much you would save.**

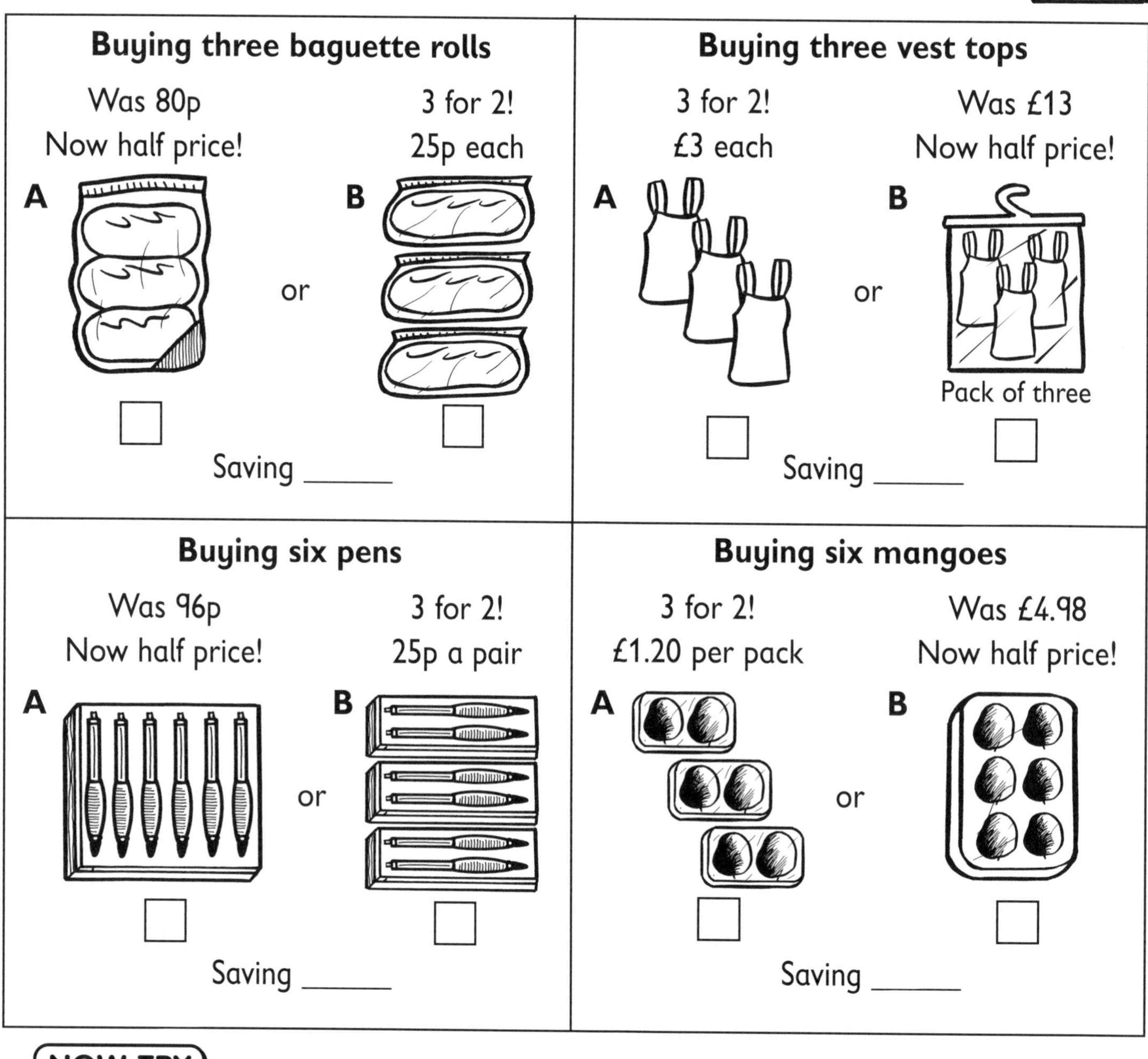

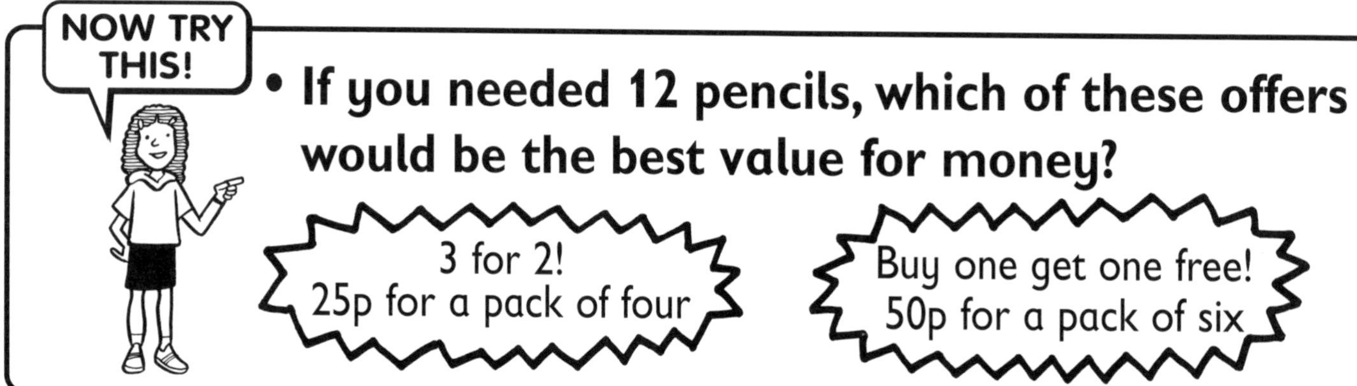

- **If you needed 12 pencils, which of these offers would be the best value for money?**

Teachers' note Before beginning the activity, ensure that the children understand what is meant by the offer '3 for 2'. Encourage the children to discuss each offer with a partner and to make judgements about which offer is the best value for money.

Marble run

On the marble run there are sections that can be opened or closed to allow the marble to carry on or to drop down.

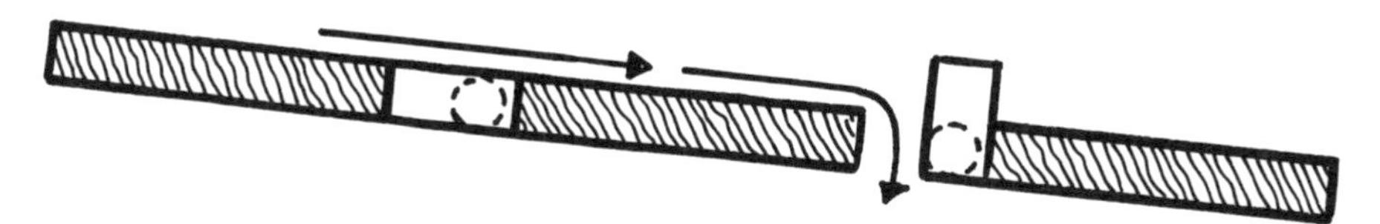

- **Find different ways that the marble can go and work out its total when it drops into a container.**

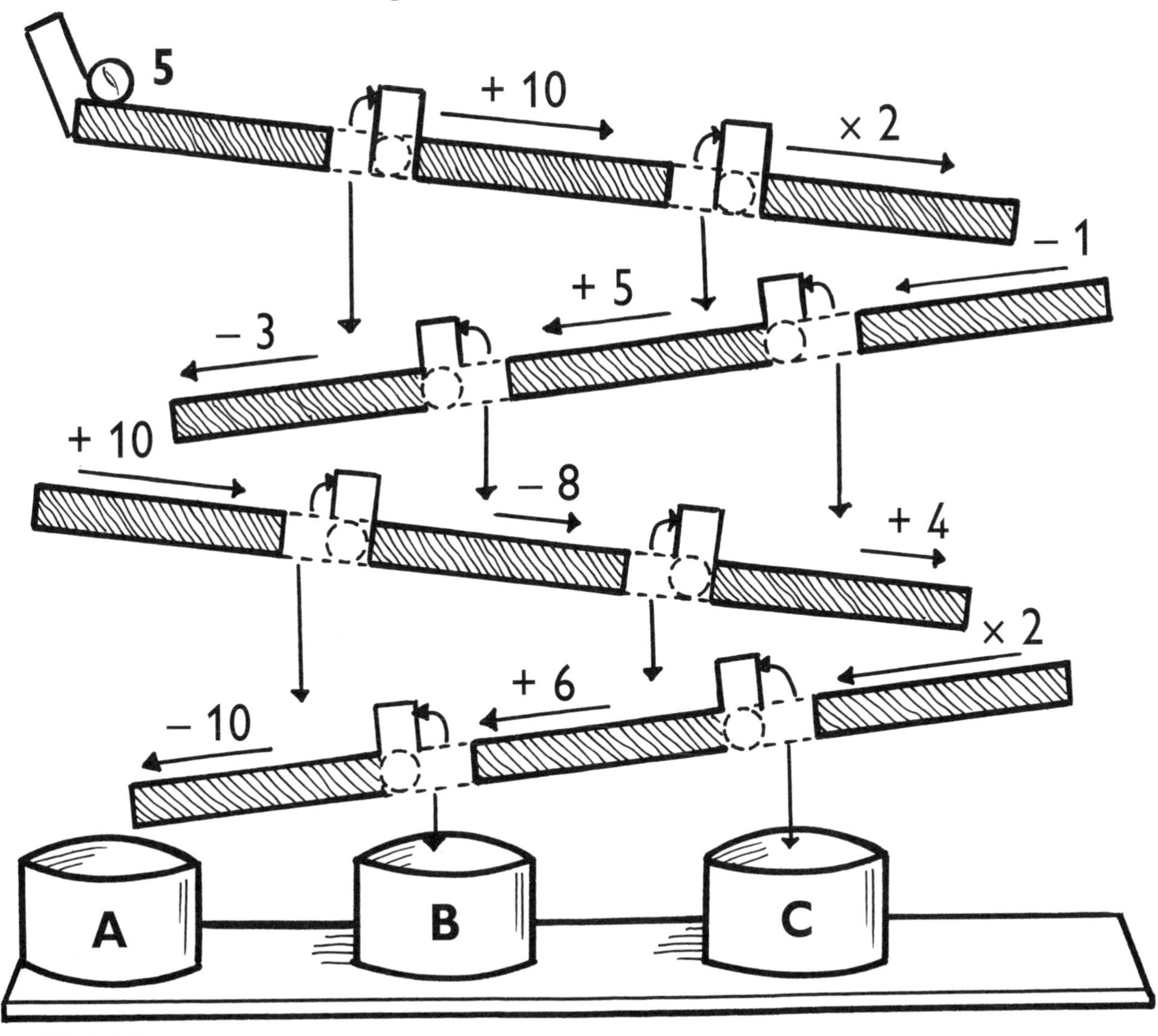

- **Can you find ways of making any of these numbers?**

10 16 32 0 12 80

Teachers' note There are many different possible numbers that can be made, starting with the marble number 5. This number could be changed to create more challenging calculations. Encourage the children to persevere to find the numbers in the extension activity, and to predict which routes are likely to give the highest or lowest numbers.

In a flap

- **Work out which number is hidden beneath each flap.**

1 $36 + 17 =$ 53

2 $12 \times 3 =$ ☐

3 $45 - 13 =$ ☐

4 $36 \div 4 =$ ☐

5 $25 + 19 =$ ☐

6 $41 - 17 =$ ☐

7 $16 +$ ☐ $= 39$

8 $13 \times$ ☐ $= 39$

9 $24 \div$ ☐ $= 3$

10 $47 -$ ☐ $= 29$

11 ☐ $\div 4 = 8$

12 ☐ $+ 38 = 81$

13 ☐ $- 40 = 63$

14 ☐ $\times 10 = 270$

~~53~~

23

32

32

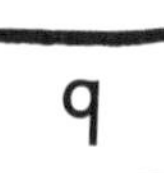

8

43

18

- **Check your answers using a different method.**

NOW TRY THIS!

- **Write four more missing number questions for a partner to solve.**

Teachers' note Encourage the children to explain how they worked out each answer, drawing particular attention to when inverse operations are used. The calculations can be altered to provide differentation.

What a puzzle!

- **Find the missing digits to make each calculation correct.**
- **Solve each puzzle and write a report on how you worked it out.**

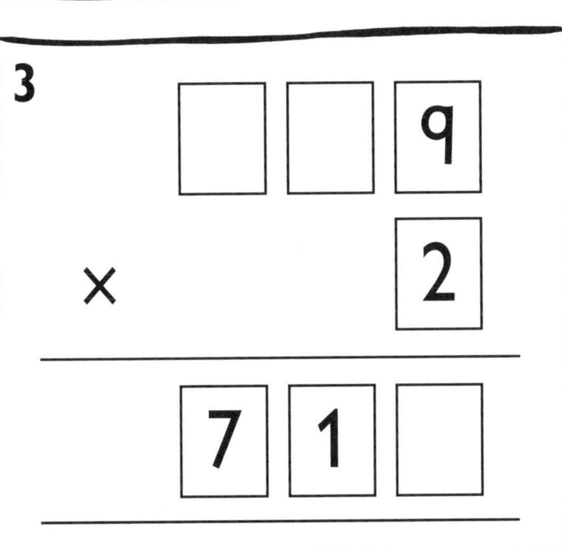

- **Write more missing number questions for a partner to solve.**

Remember, no two digits can be the same.

Teachers' note The focus of this activity should be on reporting back to the rest of the class about the strategies and reasoning used to solve the puzzles.

Grid reasoning

- **Place counters on two or more numbers in each row so that the remaining numbers in each row and column add up to 20.**

You need counters.

6	2	5	3	5	4	4	1
4	6	1	2	1	6	1	5
5	1	3	4	2	2	1	4
2	3	4	3	7	9	1	5
1	3	6	8	3	2	6	5
7	9	2	4	6	2	2	4
2	2	4	4	3	4	4	1
4	4	7	2	1	5	8	1

NOW TRY THIS!

- **Write a report on what you did and the strategies that you used.**

Teachers' note The focus of this activity should be on reporting back to others in the class about the thinking and reasoning that took place when solving the puzzle.

Answers

p 13
UNDERCOVER

p 14
1 47 **2** 60 **3** 70 **4** 45 **5** 81 **6** 49 **7** 85 **8** 45

p 15
1 £2.96 **2** £1.95 **3** £5.80 **4** £9.43 **5** £5.08 **6** £4.70

p 16
1 5 **2** 3 **3** 4 **4** 3 **5** 3 **6** 3 **7** 3 **8** 3
Now try this!
1 100 g **2** 25 g **3** 225 g **4** 325 g
5 125 g **6** 25 g **7** 277 ml **8** 275 ml

p 17
1 £1 **2** £2.40 **3** £3 **4** 60p
5 60p **6** £3.90 **7** £1.75 **8** £3.30

Now try this!
£5.47

p 18
1 £210 **2** £10 + £60, £20 + £50, £30 + £40
3 £360 **4** £10 + £20 + £30 + £60, £50 + £70,
£40 + £80 or £10 + £50 + £60, £20 + £30 + £70
£40 + £80 or £20 + £40 + £60, £50 + £70, £10 + £30 + £80

p 19
1 £360 **2** £10 + £80, £20 + £70, £30 + £60, £50 + £40
3 £450
4 £10 + £90 + £50, £20 + £70+ £60, £30 + £40 + £80
or £10 + £60 + £80, £20 + £90 + £40, £30 + £50 + £70
or £10 + £20 + £30 + £90, £40 + £50+ £60, £70 + £80
or £10 + £20 + £30 + £40 + £50, £90 + £60, £70 + £80
or £20 + £30 + £40 + £60, £10 + £50+ £90, £70 + £80
or £10 + £30 + £40 + £70, £20 + £50+ £80, £60 + £90
or £10 + £30 + £50 + £60, £20 + £40+ £90, £70 + £80
or £10 + £20 + £50 + £70, £30 + £40+ £80, £60 + £90

p 20
1 55 miles **2** 72 miles **3** 36 miles **4** 210 miles

p 21
1 800 g **2** 1.8 kg **3** 200 g **4** 100 g
5 A, B and D **6** 200 g **7** 50 g **8** 2.6 kg

Now try this!
B and C, A and D

p 22
1 1000 ml = 575 ml + 150 ml + **275 ml** **2** 960 ml ÷ 3 = **320 ml**
3 2 l = 375 ml + 375 ml + **1250 ml**
4 750 ml ÷ 2 = 375 ml , 375 ml – 100 ml = **275 ml**
5 175 ml x 4 = **700 ml**
6 150 ml x 4 = 600 ml, 600 ml + 150 ml = **750 ml**

p 23
1 880 ml ÷ 2 = 440 ml, 440 ml ÷ 2 = 220 ml, 880 ml + 440 ml + 220 ml = **1540 ml**
2 2500 ml – 300 ml = 2200 ml, 2200 ml ÷ 2 = **1100 ml**
3 3000 ml – 1600 ml = 1400 ml, 1400 ml ÷ 2 = **700 ml**
4 460 ml x 2 = 920 ml, 460 ml + 240 ml = 700 ml, 920 ml + 700 ml = **1620 ml**
5 720 ml ÷ 3 = 240 ml, 240 ml + 720 ml = **960 ml**
6 90 ml x 4 = **360 ml**

p 24
The word is BROOMSTICK.

p 25
A 6:34 pm **B** 7:00 am **C** 2:49 pm **D** 5:56 am
E 7:07 pm **F** 1:10 am **G** 3:28 am **H** 11:27 am

p 26
1 38 mins **2** 7:18 am **3** 34 mins **4** $2\frac{1}{2}$ hours
5 11:32 am **6** $1\frac{1}{4}$ hours **7** 9:13 am

p 27
Now try this!
Check that the children have used the correct unit in their answers.
1 7 **2** 41 **3** 52 **4** 10 **5** 5 **6** 18

p 28
1 + 300 **2** – 100 **3** + 20 **4** + 200
Now try this!
+ 567

p 29
1 + 12 **2** – 40 **3** – 378 **4** ÷ 2
Now try this!
x 2

p 30
1 D **2** B **3** C **4** D **5** D **6** A

p 31
1 A, B and C **2** A and B **3** B and C **4** A and C
Now try this!
8 bags

p 32
Possible answers: **1** 500 ÷ 20 = 25 **2** 32 ÷ 4 = 8, 32 – 8 = 24
3 8 x £1.25 = £10.00, £10.00 – £4.50 = £5.50
4 £1.69 + £0.70 + £1.25 = £3.64
5 1000 ml ÷ 5 = 200 ml, 200 ml x 3 = 600 ml
6 £1.69 – £0.78 = £0.91 **7** 55p x 9 = £4.95, so 9 can be bought.

p 33
Answers plus equivalents:

3 x 4 + 5 x 6 = 42	3 x 4 + 5 x 8 = 52	3 x 4 + 6 x 8 = 60
3 x 5 + 4 x 6 = 39	3 x 5 + 4 x 8 = 47	3 x 5 + 6 x 8 = 63
3 x 6 + 4 x 5 = 38	3 x 6 + 4 x 8 = 50	3 x 6 + 5 x 8 = 58
3 x 8 + 4 x 5 = 44	3 x 8 + 4 x 6 = 48	3 x 8 + 5 x 6 = 54
4 x 5 + 3 x 6 = 38	4 x 5 + 3 x 8 = 44	4 x 5 + 6 x 8 = 68
4 x 6 + 3 x 5 = 39	4 x 6 + 3 x 8 = 48	4 x 6 + 5 x 8 = 64
4 x 8 + 3 x 5 = 47	4 x 8 + 3 x 6 = 50	4 x 8 + 5 x 6 = 62
5 x 6 + 3 x 4 = 42	5 x 6 + 3 x 8 = 54	5 x 6 + 4 x 8 = 62
5 x 8 + 3 x 4 = 52	5 x 8 + 3 x 6 = 58	5 x 8 + 4 x 6 = 64
6 x 8 + 4 x 5 = 68	6 x 8 + 4 x 3 = 60	6 x 8 + 5 x 3 = 63

Now try this!
If the children attempt the extension suggested in the Teachers' note, they should find that 120 answers are possible if a '7' card is added. (There are 30 ways with four cards, and the '7' card could replace any one of the four cards in each calculation: 30 x 4 = 120.)

p 35
1 22 bottles **2** 15 days **3** 14 days **4** 200 miles
Now try this!
80 cm

p 36
All numbers from 6p to 60p can be made with six coins, and all but 38p, 39p, 48p and 49p can be made with only four coins.

p 37

Number of grapes	Total number of ways
1	1
2	2
3	4
4	8
5	16
6	32

The doubling pattern can obviously be seen, thus seven grapes would have 64 solutions and eight grapes would have 128 solutions.
The total set of solutions for five grapes and six grapes is given below.
16 solutions for five grapes:
1+1+1+1+1, 1+1+1+2, 1+1+2+1, 1+2+1+1, 2+1+1+1, 1+1+3, 1+3+1, 3+1+1, 1+4, 4+1, 1+2+2, 2+1+2, 2+2+1, 2+3, 3+2, 5

32 solutions for six grapes:
1+1+1+1+1+1, 1+1+1+1+2, 1+1+1+2+1, 1+1+2+1+1, 1+2+1+1+1, 2+1+1+1+1 1+1+1+3, 1+1+3+1, 1+3+1+1, 3+1+1+1, 1+1+4, 1+4+1, 4+1+1,
1+5, 5+1, 1+1+2+2, 1+2+1+2, 1+2+2+1, 2+2+1+1, 2+1+2+1, 2+1+1+2, 1+2+3, 1+3+2, 2+1+3, 3+1+2, 2+3+1, 3+2+1, 2+2+2, 3+3, 2+4, 4+2, 6

p 38

a 6 horses **b** 8 cows **c** 24 animals

Now try this!

The answer will depend on the multiple of 5 written into the box, but here are some possible solutions:

[5] sheep 3 horses, 4 cows, 12 animals altogether
[15] sheep 9 horses, 12 cows, 36 animals altogether
[20] sheep 12 horses, 16 cows, 48 animals altogether
[25] sheep 15 horses, 20 cows, 60 animals altogether

p 39

26 children 4 in tents A, D and E, 6 in tent B, and 8 in tent C.

p 40

1 true **2** false **3** false **4** true **5** true **6** true

p 42

There are 27 solutions to this thimble problem:

Three starting 00:	000	001	002
Three starting 01:	010	011	012
Three starting 02:	020	021	022
Three starting 10:	100	101	102
Three starting 11:	110	111	112
Three starting 12:	120	121	122
Three starting 20:	200	201	202
Three starting 21:	210	211	212
Three starting 22:	220	221	222

Now try this!

There are 10 solutions to this thimble problem:

One starting 00:	003		
Three starting 1:	111	120	102
Two starting 2:	210	201	
One starting 3:	300		
One starting 01:	012		
One starting 02:	021		
One starting 03:	030		

p 46

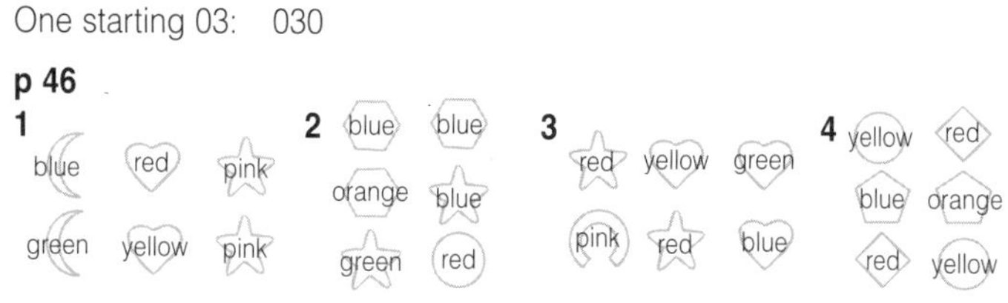

p 47 and p 48

Set 1 solution:	camcorder	photo album	batteries
	DVDs	camera	memory card
	tripod	rucksack	binoculars
Set 2 solution:	photo album	binoculars	camcorder
	DVDs	memory card	batteries
	camera	rucksack	tripod
Set 3 solution:	binoculars	DVDs	tripod
	camcorder	photo album	camera
	batteries	rucksack	memory card

p 49

3	8	6	14
5	10	10	20
8	13	16	29
6	11	12	23

⬡ = □ + ○

Now try this!

2	4	6	12
1	2	3	6
7	14	21	42
8	16	24	48

Possible rules:

⬡ = ○ x 2 ⬡ = □ x 3 ⬡ = △ x 6 ⬡ = (□ + △) x 2

p 50

1 17, 20, 23, 26, 29, 32, 35, 38, 41 **2** 9, 13, 17, 21, 25, 29, 33, 37, 41
3 3, 8, 13, 18, 23, 28, 33, 38, 43 **4** 1, 7, 13, 19, 25, 31, 37, 43, 49
5 2, 7, 12, 17, 22, 27, 32, 37, 42 **6** 2, 5, 8, 11, 14, 17, 20, 23, 26
7 22, 26, 30, 34, 38, 42, 46, 50, 54 **8** 5, 11, 17, 23, 29, 35, 41, 47, 53

p 51

The shaded shapes are Ali's and the unshaded shapes are Sally's.

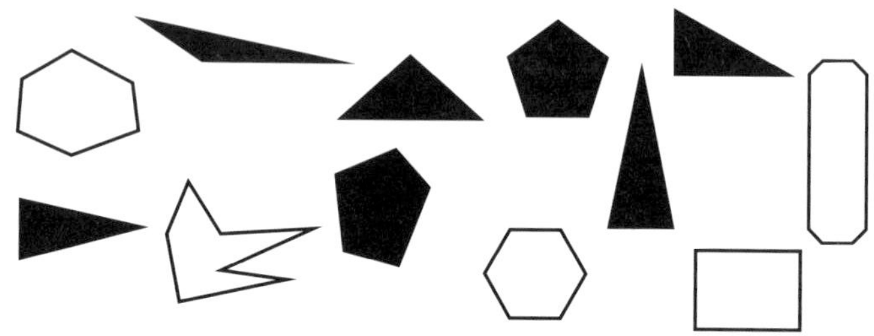

p 53

6 is a factor of 54 9 is a factor of 54 6 multiplied by 9 = 54
9 multiplied by 6 = 54 54 is the product of 6 and 9
54 is the product of 9 and 6 54 is a multiple of 6
54 is a multiple of 9 54 divided by 6 = 9 54 divided by 9 = 6

p 54

Hussain 50 Jane 21 Jermaine 28 Benny 27 Jenny 35 Penny 18

Now try this!

32: 1, 2, 4, 8, 16, 32

p 55

1 true **2** false **3** false **4** true

p 56

1 even **2** odd **3** odd **4** odd **5** even **6** odd **7** even **8** even **9** even **10** even

p 57

1 +10 **2** +9 **3** +11 **4** +5 **5** +8 **6** +9

p 58

1 A saving 10p **2** A saving 50p **3** A saving 2p **4** A saving 9p

Now try this!

They are both the same value.

p 60

1 53 **2** 36 **3** 32 **4** 9 **5** 44 **6** 24 **7** 23
8 3 **9** 8 **10** 18 **11** 32 **12** 43 **13** 103 **14** 27

p 61

(Several solutions are possible for **1** and **2**)

1 e.g. 357 + 62 = 419 **2** e.g. 935 − 71 = 864 **3** 359 x 2 = 718 **4** 834 x 9 = 7506

p 62

Row 1, cover 5 and 5; Row 2, cover 4 and 2; Row 3, cover 1 and 1; Row 4, cover 9 and 5; Row 5, cover 8 and the second 6; Row 6, cover 7 and 9; Row 7, cover 3 and 1; Row 8, cover 7 and 5